Viz

All aboard

The

Thick Repeater

A donkey-rigged skin-boat bulging at the bulwarks with the plunder of issues 88-93

Able Seamen: Alex Collier, Chris Donald, Simon Donald, Graham Dury, Davey Jones and Simon Thorp.
Boatswain: Steve Donald *Midshipmen:* Simon Ecob, John Fardell, Jolly Roger Radio.
Cabin Boy: Steve Olive. *Powder Monkeys:* Sheila Thompson, Stevie Glover. *Man overboard:* Spatts Patterson.
Man in the barrel: Ed Axon.
Man poking his little posh cock through the hole in the barrel: John Brown

ISBN No. 1 902212 320

Published in Great Britain by
Long John Silver Brown Publishing
The New Brigantinehouse
136 ~ 142 Bramley Road
Treasure Island
W10 6SR

First, and quite likely last printing September 2000

Copyright JBP. All rights reserved. No part of this book may be reproduced, copied, transmitted or used to deliver a black spot to Blind Pugh in any manner or by any means without written permission on an ancient and faded treasure map from the publisher and his parrot.

Printed in Great Britain, me hearties.

Letterbocks

A 'Titanic' page upon the ocean
of ideas, thoughts and strong emotion
Write to us with what you're thinking
Cos this mag is fucking sinking

Thorough-fare point

❏ All roads lead to Rome, or so they say. Not the A57. I drove along it the other day and ended up in Worksop.

**Chas Newman
Sheffield**

❏ Sir Bob Geldof , who wrote the line "There won't be snow in Africa this Christmas" has obviously never been up mount Kilimanjairo.

**M. Boardman
Stockport**

❏ Had Jeanette Krankie been on board the Titanic she would have been the safest passenger on the ship. When they manned the lifeboats and the cry went out for "Women and children first", she would have qualified under both categories.

**Edward Semi
Norwich**

Letterbocks
PO Box 1PT
Newcastle upon Tyne
NE99 1PT
Fax: 0191 2414244
viz.comic@virgin.net

❏ If the Church of England is serious about preventing congregations from dwindling any further perhaps they could think about doing the communion wafers, which represent the body of Christ, in a range of popular 'snack' flavours, such as salt'n'vinegar, or smokey bacon. And instead of communion wine, how about a selection of cocktails, and communion alcopops for the kids. I'd welcome the views of vicars on this subject.

**P. Sprout
Burnley**

You Asda laugh

❏ I was shopping in Asda recently when I spotted a sign above the check-out saying 'Your Problems Are Our Problems'. I had to laugh, because I'm due to appear in court next week on three charges of shoplifting.

**T.B.
Swindon**

Crappy Days

❏ In response to Derek Knox (issue 86) who asked why the Fonz is considered cool despite the company he keeps. The Fonz is cool precisely because be hangs around with fuckwits like Cunningham, Potsy and Ralph Malph. If he were to hang around with James Dean, Jimi Hendrix and Jim Morrison, he would look a complete cunt.

**Johnny Wood
e-mail**

❏ Opponents of fox hunting foolishly suggest that drag hunting would be an adequate replacement for our sport. Well I for one would take no pleasure from hunting foxes dressed in women's clothing.

**E.B. Poole
Northumberland**

❏ I thought the local council had gone too far with their traffic calming measures when I drove over a 'sleeping policemen' on the drive outside my house. Then I realised, it was my husband. He is a police officer and had nodded off in his deck chair after doing some gardening.
Luckily the doctors saw the funny side, although they tell me my husband may never walk again.

**Mrs B. Idiot
Hove**

Snow joke

❏ I went bobsleighing this Christmas. I killed Bob Holness, Bob Monkhouse and Bob Carolgees. Do any other readers have jokes that work better when said out aloud as opposed to written down?

**Alex Walsh-Atkins
Moseley, Birmingham**

❏ Is it just me, or is Casualty not funny anymore?

**James Richmond
e-mail**

Corny

❏ I think anyone who pays to see a chiropodist needs to have their feet examined. Or something like that.

**John O'Connor
e-mail**

TOP TIPS

ANGLERS. Attach a helium balloon to your line and bait the hook with an acorn. Then sit under a tree and 'fish' for squirrels. An upturned laundry basket would make an ideal keep net, but don't forget to throw the squirrels back into the tree at the end of the day.

G. Mansion
West Hampstead

A STAMP stuck to the side of a matchbox makes an ideal 'mini-TV' on which pet mice can 'watch' the Queen's speech.

Mr V. Mews
Mayfair

COLLECT all the loose breadcrumbs from the bottom of fish finger boxes etc. You'll be surprised at how quickly you'll have enough to make a new loaf.

J. T.
Thropton

A MOUSE trap placed on top of your alarm clock will prevent you from rolling over and going back to sleep.

Tom Rice
Edinburgh

ADVENTUROUS lovers. Sprinkle talcum powder on each other's rings, then lie on the floor and fart up in the air to send each other sexy 'bum-smoke signals' across the bedroom.

Adrian Bond
London SE7

MAKE money go further. Post it to a distant relative and ask them to send it back again.

Gayle
Epworth

FEED bees oranges. Hey presto! They make marmalade instead of honey.

John Tait
Thropton

GENTLEMEN. Gauge the outside temperature using a 'plumometer'. Open your flies and dangling your plums in front of an open letterbox. If they shrink it is cold outside, if they go baggy it is warm, and if they remain the same size it is the same temperature outside as it is in the house.

A. Newman
Castleford

ADD a spoonful of wallpaper paste to tea or coffee before serving for safer, 'non-drip' beverages.

John Tait
Thropton

FLU sufferers. Spit your colourful phlegm into a lemonade bottle then pop it on top of your TV. Hey presto. A fashionable sixties style lava lamp.

Haydn C. Vickerman
Macclesfield

MAKE use of Christmas tree lights all year round. Lay them on the floor between your bed and the toilet. Hey presto! Runway style lights to guide you safely towards the lavatory at night.

Tom Rice
Edinburgh

LEMSIP sachets make ideal 'sherbet dips' to cheer up ill relatives.

Greg Wigg
Toddington, Glos.

Well Knock Me Down! with A. Feather

Chronic sleepwalker Mr Xiang Wok Pong awoke one morning to find himself on the moon! The 112-year-old bicycle shop owner from China's Guangdong Province had risen in the night and cycled onto a Florida-bound Jumbo Jet at Panyu Airport. On landing, he pedalled off, still fast asleep and somehow boarded a Saturn V rocket on the launch-pad at Cape Canaveral. Red-faced officials at Mission Control had to admit a lapse in security when they spotted Mr. Pong in his pyjamas, riding round the lunar surface, snoring happily!

The Collins family from Basingstoke thought they had seen the last of their pet tortoise, Monty, when they emigrated to Australia, leaving the reptile with the new owners of their house. But loyal Monty had other ideas and set out on a fantastic journey to the other side of the world to be reunited with his owners. Against all odds, he turned up on the doorstep of their house in Moony Ponds, Sydney on September 8th 1994. However, the Collins family had seen the last of him. Their tortoise had taken 310 years to complete the 12,000 mile journey and they had all been dead for some 250 years.

Prison Governor Draylon Hogg from Texas, Wyoming, USA, was killed by his dog Duke in a bizarre accident. Hapless Hogg sat down for a cup of coffee in Dade County Jail's electric chair when the 2-year-old pointer's wagging tail hit the 'ON' button, sending 15,000 volts through his master's body, killing him instantly in about twenty minutes. In a bizarre footnote, Hogg's brother Nylon who adopted Duke also fell victim to the jinxed animal when it killed him with a bow and arrow while playing in the garden.

Whilst sailing to France on her honeymoon in 1941, Mrs Edna Potter fell overboard after a decktop blindfold trampoline prank by her husband Sidney went tragically wrong. Heartbroken, Mr Potter returned to Britain alone, and spent the next fifty years as a virtual recluse. In July 1991, on what would have been their Golden wedding anniversary, he sat down to his usual solitary supper of fish and chips. However, when he cut into the haddock, he saw something glinting inside. Amazingly, it was his wife. She stepped out of the fish and embraced her astonished husband for the first time in half a century. Their reunion meal was cut tragically short, however, when Mr. Potter choked to death on his mushy peas. At the autopsy, the pathologist spotted something lodged in the corpse's throat, and was astounded to see his own wedding ring, which he had lost in a pea field 20 years ago to the day!

Arthur Feather is the Professor of Strange Facts at Oxford University

THE BUSTER BLOODVESSEL STORY - PART 1

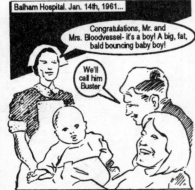

Balham Hospital. Jan. 14th, 1961...

Congratulations, Mr. and Mrs. Bloodvessel- it's a boy! A big, fat, bald bouncing baby boy!

We'll call him Buster

From an early age, Buster dreamed of only one thing- Pop Stardom!

I wish I could think of a name for my band. Then we'd get famous and go on Top of the Pops.

Buster! Don't slouch. And take your elbows off the table...it's bad manners!

Wait a minute!... That's it!!

And 10 years later his dream came true, when he appeared on Top of the Pops in a big dress

TOP OF THE POPS

Lip up, Fatty! Oh, lip up, Fatty! Fatty reggae!

5

Part 2- As the hits dry up, Buster hits the cake shop!

GARRY BUSHELL THE BEAR

ONE WINTERS DAY IN THE FOREST

GARRY'S CAVE. HIBERNATING: DO NOT DISTURB

SNORE

HERE'S AN EMPTY CAVE, HANK. WE'LL STOP IN HERE FOR A BREATHER

GARRY'S CAVE. HIBERNATING: DO NOT DISTURB

NEXT DOOR

SNORE

HUH? WHAT'S THAT NOISE?

CLUMP BUMP

SOUNDS LIKE SOMEONES MOVING INTO THE NEXT CAVE. I WONDER WHO IT IS

KNOWING MY LUCK, IT'LL BE A FAMILY OF BLOODY POLAR BEARS

NOT THAT I'VE GOT ANYTHING AGAINST POLARS. BUT THEY COME OVER HERE, THEY TAKE ALL THE FISH. BREED LIKE RABBITS, TOO

I'LL PROBABLY BE KEPT AWAKE ALL NIGHT BY THEIR LOUD RHYTHMIC POLAR BEAR MUSIC

THEY'RE NOT THE SAME AS US BROWN BEARS, SEE. IT'S A CULTURAL THING

I'M NOT STANDING FOR THIS

I'M GOING TO WRITE ABOUT IT IN MY WEEKLY COLUMN FOR THE WOODLAND GAZETTE

"NO ONE CAN ACCUSE ME OF BEING SPECIESIST.."

TAP TAP TAP TAP TAP TAP TAP

".. BUT I'M A BROWN BEAR, AND I'M PROUD OF MY KODIAK IDENTITY."

"...AND I'D RATHER BEND OVER FOR THE BUBBLE-BATH IN BARRYMORE'S BATHROOM THAN LET MY DAUGHTER MARRY A POLAR BEAR..."

TAP TAP TAP TAP TAP TAP -CHING

GARRY'S CAVE. HIBERNATING: DO NOT DISTURB

TAP TAP TAP TAP TAP TAP

".. WE SHOULD PUT THEM ON THE NEXT FOX'S GLACIER MINT BOAT AND SEND 'EM ALL BACK WHERE THEY CAME FROM"

THERE. THAT'LL TEACH THEM TO MOVE INTO MY NEIGHBOURHOOD

HM. EVERYTHING HAS GONE STRANGELY QUIET NEXT DOOR

COME TO THINK OF IT, I'VE NOT HEARD ANY SOUNDS OF KIDS SINCE THEY MOVED IN

PERHAPS THEY'RE NOT A FAMILY OF POLAR BEARS AFTER ALL. PERHAPS THEY'RE A COUPLE OF GRIZZLY BEAR HOMOSEXUALS

WELL THEY'RE NOT GETTING ANYWHERE NEAR **THIS** BROWN BEAR'S BROWNEYE, THAT'S FOR SURE

(YAWN) AH WELL. BEST GET BACK TO SLEEP

FIVE MINUTES LATER

IT TURNS MY STOMACH TO IMAGINE WHAT THOSE LIMP-PAWED GRIZZLY BEAR BUM-BANDITS ARE GETTING UP TO IN THE NEXT CAVE

THERE'LL BE MORE MINCING GOING ON THAN IN A MR KIPLING PIE FACTORY IN THE RUN-UP TO CHRISTMAS

"THESE SO-CALLED GAY GRIZZLYS ARE TURNING OUR ONCE-PROUD FOREST INTO A PERVERTS PLAYGROUND.."

TAP TAP TAP TAP TAP TAP TAP TAP

"..THERE ARE MORE WOOFTERS IN THESE WOODS THAN IN BATTERSEA DOGS HOME.."

"I FOR ONE DON'T WANT MY CUBS GETTING TOUCHED UP BY SOME LISPING TAIL-LIFTER.."

GARRY'S CAVE. HIBERNAT DO NOT DI

TAP TAP TAP -CHING

I'D RATHER BEND OVER FOR THE SOAP IN JULIE BURCHILL'S JACUZZI ...ERM. IF SHE HAD A COCK WHICH SHE PROBABLY HAS

I'VE GOT A READERSHIP OF FOUR MILLION WOODLAND ANIMALS AND AN I.Q. OF 220

GARRY'S CAVE. HIBERNAT DO NOT DI

SO PUT THAT IN YOUR POLITICALLY CORRECT PIPE AND SMOKE IT

OH YES, I BET MY NEW NEIGHBOURS ARE A RIGHT BUNCH OF POLITICALLY CORRECT LOONY LEFT-WING EXTREMISTS

THEY PROBABLY WANT TO BAN US ALL FROM CATCHING FISH BECAUSE IT'S A 'BLOOD SPORT'

COBBLERS! I'VE BEEN A SALMON EATER ALL MY LIFE, AND I'M NOT GIVING UP NOW

FISHING HAS BEEN A PROUD BROWN BEAR TRADITION IN THIS FOREST FOR UNTOLD GENERATIONS

THAT DOES IT! IF THOSE BEAR LEFTIES THINK THEY CAN COME INTO MY FOREST AND TAKE AWAY MY RIGHTS, THEY CAN THINK AGAIN

I'M GOING TO SORT THEM OUT ONCE AND FOR ALL

NOBODY'S FORCING **ME** TO GIVE UP FISH

SAY NO TO BAN ON BLOODSPORTS

MARCH

IF THEY LIKE COMMUNISM SO MUCH WHY DON'T THEY GO AND LIVE IN RUSSIA?

BANG!

URK!

LATER

"WORLD OF RUGS"

-NEW- GENUINE BEARSKIN RUG £49.99

SHORTLY

"WORLD OF RUGS"

-NEW- GENUINE BEARSKIN RUG £49.99 SOLD

AND

SOCIETY FOR GLOBAL POLITICAL CORRECTNESS -HEADQUARTERS-

"...SO THAT'S AGREED. WE'LL ABOLISH NATIONALISM, SET UP A MULTI-CULTURAL SOCIALIST REPUBLIC AND ELECT JO BRAND AS PRESIDENT"

NOW THEN. WHO FANCIES A BIT OF LESBIAN AND GAY SEX ON THE BEARSKIN RUG?

BAH!

9

GOODBYE AND GOD BLESS

Queen bids sad farewell to Royal cooker

THE Queen and other members of the Royal family gathered at Buckingham Palace yesterday to say a final farewell to the electric cooker which has served them so well for over 40 years.

There were tearful scenes at the brief decommissioning ceremony during which the Queen was seen to cry a lot more than she did at Diana's funeral..

Boil

The Royal cooker, commissioned in 1954 from the Revo factory in Tipton, was first used by the Queen to boil some potatoes on the day of her Coronation. Since then the cooker has roasted joints for visiting foreign dignitaries, baked cakes for Royal garden parties, and fried breakfasts for four generations of Royals on her spotless triple hob.

Wart

But last week another element went, and now with only one hob working the Treasury has decided that the high cost of maintaining such an old piece of kitchen equipment could not be justified.

Mole

Yesterday the cooker, still looking resplendent in its glazed white livery with black handles, it's stainless steel splashback glistening in the sunlight, was carried out the back door by a member of the Royal household staff, and dumped on the back lawn. From there she will begin her final journey next week, to the local skips.

Ratty

The Government put forward several proposals to save the cooker which has served the Royal family so well, and has become a symbol of British light engineering in the West Midlands. Plans had included advertising it for five pounds in the local free newspaper, taking it to a second hand shop, or asking a bloke who fixes washing machines if he could mend it. But a re-fit was considered too expensive.

Toad

Several Royals believe it would be 'inappropriate' if their cooker was to fall into private hands, and last week Princess Ann was quoted as saying it should be chucked into the river Thames. She fears that gypsies may remove the cooker from the skips, and that new owners would not be able to maintain her to the same high standards that the Queen had maintained throughout the years

Badger

"Mum always ensures that the trays are frequently removed and steeped in detergent, and that the insides of the oven cleaned with Mr Muscle", the horsey bint is believed to have told friends.

Pester

As yet the Government has not announced any plans to replace the Royal cooker. The cost of a new one - estimated to be over £400 - is thought to be excessive, although several private initiatives have already been launched to fund a replacement.

Hector

These include a local retailer who proposes a 'buy now, pay later' scheme whereby a new cooker could be bought on interest free credit with no payments until June 1998. Meanwhile a business consortium headed by Harrods boss Mohammed Al Fayed has offered to finance the purchase of a second hand replacement for fifty quid from a local auction. However, privately the Queen is thought to oppose the idea of a dodgy, second hand cooker.

Happier days - In 1955, shortly after her Coronation, the Queen knocks up some soup on the Royal Revo cooker before nipping out to change the guards.

I'M SORRY, TOMKINS. I'M GOING TO HAVE TO LET YOU GO

10

THE CRITICS

Panel 1: Ah! That new play which we gave a damning review last week has closed down... / Excellent! It's so gratifying to find that the objective voice of the critic still has some influence...

Panel 2: Of course I knew the play wouldn't be any good... I'd not even heard of the author, Steven somebody-or-other... He certainly wasn't up at Cambridge with anyone I know. / Quite!.. We obviously made the right decision not to waste time going to see the play before we wrote our review.

Panel 3: Now, I've managed to get us a new weekly column.... A restaurant review for the Sunday Tome's Lifestyle section. / How exciting! A new challenge!... After all, food is the new art!

Panel 4: Now, where shall we eat this week?... One must be daring... Blaze a trail away from the fashionable metropolitan scene... Seek out fresh new culinary talent... / I know just the place...

Panel 5: Orlando! So this is your new place!

Panel 6: Crispin! Natasha! "MWAH!"... Haven't seen you since dear Binky's little soirée last week... Welcome to chez moi, ha ha!.. I'll get Steve, my head waiter, to attend to you...

Panel 7: Come along, Steve! Stop daydreaming! There's work to be done! / Yeah, sorry boss... I'm just really depressed about that play I wrote closing down... I thought I'd be able to become a full time writer.

Panel 8: Well sorry, dear boy, but you're still a waiter and there are tables to serve... Natasha and Crispin Critic have come to review us for their new column...

Panel 9: Natasha and Crispin Critic?!...They're the bastards who killed my play!

Panel 10: We'll start with the truffle-filled filo-parcels in jus d'avocado...

Panel 11: Right!. I'll not bother the kitchen with their order... I'll prepare their meal myself... Heh heh!

Panel 12: Exquisite! The paper-thin filo pastry conceals an exotically dark, almost smokey interior.... / The swirling green jus has a subtle, organic flavour...

Panel 13: I don't believe it! They've actually eaten it! / That was superb!.. Now we'll try the caramelised quails' breasts in calf's liver ragu on a bed of wild seaweed...

Panel 14: Hah! Let's see them try to eat this!

Panel 15: A triumph! A veritable kaleidoscope of daringly high, even pungent flavours. / One applauds the renaissance of simple country cooking...

Panel 16: Now, we must try one of Orlando's famous puddings... / We'll have the chocolate noisettes drizzled with lemon sauce.

Panel 17: Right!...This calls for desperate measures!... Two chocolate noisettes drizzled with lemon sauce, coming up!

Panel 18: Ah! This is how chocolate should taste... Dark, bitter, so unlike the over-sweetened rubbish we so often get in Britain... / The sour, steaming sauce transports one's tastebuds to new realms of sensation...

Panel 19: Dear Orlando has surpassed himself as usual... Now, how about a cup of the dark-roast Tibetan coffee to finish with?

Panel 20: GET YOUR OWN BLOODY TIBETAN COFFEE, YOU STUPID LITTLE PARASITES!! SHALLOW, IGNORANT LITTLE SHITS!!

Panel 21: How wonderful! Orlando didn't tell us he was running theatre here, too. / A solo actor confronts the audience with an angry, Osbornesque monologue...

Panel 22: A powerful new voice in dramatic writing... / Did you write the monologue yourself? You should try writing a play, you know.

John Fardell '98

13

SCROUNGING BASTARDS!

MEET the Dougan family. Husband Bill and wife Doreen are Britain's biggest scroungers.

They pocket an amazing £120 a week in handouts, and live a life of luxury in a three bedroom house - paid for by the council.

By
RAB. L. ROWSER
and LIN SCHMOBB

This family deserve to DIE

All smiles as the Dougan family pose for our conniving photographer outside their house yesterday, unaware of the editorial direction our reporters intended to take.

Wannabe's

Bill hasn't done a single days work in the two years since he was blinded and partially paralysed in a car accident. He claims he's not fit for employment. But he still manages to get to his door mat once a week where he picks up a whopping £85 state benefits cheque for so-called 'invalidity'. Unable to walk, he sits at home on his arse all day, counting his cash.

Bumble bees

Dole family Dougan claim to be hard up - yet they still have TWO children. And soon there'll be more. They breed like RABBITS, and yo-yo knickered slut Doreen, 28, is hoping for ANOTHER sprog later this year, leaving tax payers like YOU to fork out another £12 a week in child benefit.

Humble cheese

Perhaps next time she should spend some of it on contraceptives.

Humble pie

Free school milk for their ugly brood costs YOU the taxpayer another £2 a week. Yet bone-idle Bill, 33, still wants MORE. "It's difficult getting by on benefits, and I'd like to be able to provide better for my children", the grasping git told our reporter.

Kids Michael, 9, and Angela, 5, have already jumped on the benefits gravy train. Like their work-shy parents they expect something for nothing and collect a thumping 50p a week EACH in pocket money.

Blind Faith

Their house is crammed with tell tale signs of their cushy lifestyle. In the kitchen Mrs Dougan offered us a cup of "tea or coffee". Oh yes. The big spending Dougans have BOTH. Their fancy Swan kettle probably set them back £20, and a swish pedal bin in the corner must have cost thirty or forty quid.

Steeleye Span

But then that's hardly surprising. Because wife Doreen isn't short of a few bob. She works nights as a cleaner, picking up a hefty £42 a week as well as cleaning up on state hand outs. Nice work if you can get it.

Steely Dan

But still she MOANS. "What I'd really like is to take the family on holiday", she told us. "We've never been away at all since before we were married". But wait a minute. That's not all.

Desperate Dan

"With Bill unable to work, I'd like to go out and pursue a career of my own. But its difficult finding people to look after the kids", said the money grabbing bitch as she sat there, sipping her expensive Nescafe coffee and offering us fancy chocolate biscuits like there was no tomorrow.

Lord Snooty

Doreen's weekly shopping bill comes to £60, and she claims it's hard to make ends meet - despite raking in POUNDS in discount vouchers at the supermarket check-out. And the whining sow isn't even happy with her FREE council home. "One day I'd like to own a house of our own, with a garden for the kids to play in", groaned the grasping trollop.

Lord Snowdon

Last night a senile Tory MP stopped wanking for five minutes to BLAST the Dougans before we'd even told him anything about them: "These people are a disease on our society", he ranted drunkenly. "Why should the taxpayer fund their disgusting, depraved lifestyles? They should send them back where they came from, and beyond".

Mount Snowdon

A spokesman for the Labour party failed to say anything that we could use out of context, despite several cleverly weighted questions.

WHAT DO YOU THINK?

WE'VE whipped up our ignorant readers into a bigoted frenzy of hatred. Here's the kind of hand outs THEY'D like to see doled out to the money grabbing Dougans.

"I think it's disgusting", said Dawn Shitehouse, bulldog faced moron mother of six. *"Their house is better than mine. People like that don't even deserve to die, never mind live"*, she added.

"They should tattoo the words FILTHY SCUM BASTARDS on their foreheads and put their children in a mental home", said neighbour Edna Pigshit who gets 20p an hour LESS than Mrs Dougan at her cleaning job. *"They're just vermin that's what they are. Hanging's too good for 'em. They should string 'em up, and throw away the key"*.

"Cut his cock off and make him eat it", said disabled war veteran Joe Mengler, 82, of Leeds. Plucky Joe, who lost all his teeth biting a U boat, gets by on a paltry 2p a week army pension and is regularly mugged in his home by glue sniffers. *"And I'd pull the lever myself"*, he added.

"They should cook him in his own blood, and make him eat himself, then stone him to death with his own knackers", said taxi driver Ron Bigot, 32, who works a 60 hour week and comes home with less than £200 since all the foreigners came over here and took all the jobs, and the women. *"If he has any more babies the doctors should pop their heads with their fingers, like baby rats"*, he added.

Ring our HATE LINE

Have YOUR neighbours got a nicer house than you? Do they appear to be better off than you are? Or perhaps their garden is a mess, or their kids have got snotty noses. Ring us today on 0171 922 7386 and tell us about your nightmare neighbours. Perhaps we can arrange for a lynching. Ring us today. There's dozens of jumped up little cunt reporters fresh out of college and with no morals whatsoever waiting to take your call.

JOYRIDING / JUMPER JOKE

PULL OVER

CARDIGAN

EEEEEEEEEH!

RADIO 97

YEAHHHHH

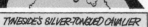

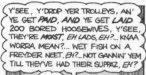

Tipton-khamen!

West Midlands Egyptian burial plan for 'One and Only' Hawkes

Ambitious plans to bury Chesney Hawkes in a latter day 'Valley Of The Kings' have sparked controversy among residents and planners in the town of Tipton.

Hawkes (right) whose pop career ended so young.

The Tipton Gateway Trust, an independent partnership of local businesses, have put forward plans for a giant tomb and pyramid to be constructed on derelict industrial land adjacent to the A457. The £50 million project will involve tunnelling a series of inter linking catacombs beneath the ground and building a spectacular stone pyramid 800 feet tall.

Chamber

In a giant burial chamber directly beneath the pyramid the body of the boy pop star Chesney Hawkes will be laid to rest in an ornate sarcophagus, surrounded by his most treasured possessions, including a gold disc, a mountain bike and his CD collection. The name of his hit single 'The One And Only' is to be carved on the wall in hieroglyphics, and the chamber will be decorated with a hand painted wall frieze depicting his appearances on Top Of The Pops.

Pop

There are further plans to bury more pop stars nearby on the same site as and when they become available, and for a landscaping scheme to create a genuine 'Valley of the Kings'. It is estimated that tourists visiting the tombs could bring an extra £300 million into the West Midlands economy every year.

Classical

Project coordinator Hugo Guthrie got the inspiration for his scheme during a holiday in Egypt. "My wife and I were visiting the pyramids and were impressed by the sheer volume of visitors they attract from all over the world. It dawned on me that a pyramid would be an ideal attraction for Tipton, and an economic boost for the whole of the Metropolitan Borough of Dudley".

Jazz

It is hoped to have the tomb built, buried under tons of sand and then rediscovered and opened to the public in time for the millennium. But the ambitious scheme has already faced criticism. Opponents say the pyramid will create car parking problems for local residents and they claim that vital wildlife habitat will be destroyed. "Mice and pigeons regularly use that land for recreational purposes", one objector told told us.

An artists impression of the Tipton pyramids development due to open in the year 2000

Boy pop king set for Midlands tomb

But Mr Guthrie remains optimistic. "Too often Tipton has been caught lacking in ambition. Now is the time to change that. The Tipton Valley of the Kings will be one of the wonders of the West Midlands. It will put us firmly back on the tourism map".

Porn

The outcome of applications for funding to the National Lottery, the Millennium Commission and English Heritage are not due for several months. Meanwhile Chesney Hawkes was last night unavailable for comment.

Joe's 90

FORMER TV star Joe 90 celebrated his 90th birthday yesterday with a quiet party at a retirement home in Filey, North Yorkshire.

Joe, who during the sixties starred in his own television show, has not been able to walk unassisted since his leg strings snapped in the late eighties. But staff at the Bay View retirement home say that he's in good spirits, and was able to enjoy a glass of champagne to celebrate his birthday.

Then and now. 90 in 68 (above) and (below) in 98 90 at 90 yesterday.

Scan

90's wife Rhapsody Angel out of Captain Scarlet died in 1992 following a long bout of woodworm. Joe was forced to sell the giant food mixer in which he sat at the beginning of his TV show to pay for her funeral. The couple had no children.

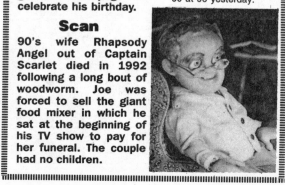

the KING of SHEDS

29 PER SQUARE FOOT

THE "VALE" WANEY ELM GARDEN SHED 12.7ft. x 5ft

Send for list of other Bargains:

Letterbocks

It's the letters page that takes 2 hours to get wood - and then goes off after 3 pushes.

❏ So, the Government plan to make reading tests tougher for school children. This could be done overnight by simply replacing our facile 26 letter alphabet with the several thousand complicated characters used by the Chinese.

**R. Perry
Southend**

Doctor in the blouse

❏ Women are a bunch of hypocrites. One minute they're carrying kidney donor cards around with them quite happy to donate all of their organs to medical research. But the minute a doctor or a dentist tries to feel them up a bit while they're under the gas they go running to the police.

**Dr P. Hammond-Organ
(struck off)
Fulchester**

Letterbocks
PO Box 1PT
Newcastle upon Tyne
NE99 1PT

Fax: 0191 2414244
viz.comic@virgin.net

❏ My father and I have been making our own jam for nearly twenty years. But in all that time we've never allowed my mother or sister to help or taste the results. We believe it should remain a male preserve.

**E. A. Browse
Westcliffe-On-Sea, Essex**

Bra-vo

❏ My wife went to get fitted for a bra recently and discovered that she's got 'Double G' tits. Pretty amazing eh? And she's not fat either. I think she deserves a fiver for that, don't you?

**Luke Gregory
London SE28**

❏ I had to laugh at something my son said the other day. Mind you, he's Chubby Brown.

**Mrs Ida Brown
Middlesbrough**

❏ If any of your readers are ever on a live television show featuring Uri Geller and he asks you to draw a picture so that he can use his psychic powers to draw an exact copy, draw a picture of a big, hairy, veiny cock and watch the spooky bastard squirm.

**James Lennox
Glasgow**

❏ I know this is supposed to be the year of the Tiger, but I'm still writing Dragon on all my cheques.

**Mark Fung-Po
Stockport**

❏ Ball gazing Lottery loser Mystic fucking Meg tried to scrounge a light off me in The Malt Shovel pub the other night to light up her Camel cigarette. I didn't have a light on me, but surely she should have known that before she asked.

**Geoff Poole
North Somerset**

Another fine mess

❏ I wonder if any of your readers could help me. I am seeking sponsors to help me pay the latest fine handed to me by Weston Magistrates Court (£75, for committing a 'Public Order' offence while drunk). If anyone could help, in return for your sponsorship I will gladly mention you or your company name the next time I am up before the magistrates.

**Andy Quinn
Weston-super-Mare**

❏ In response to Chas Newman's disappointment at finding Worksop and not Rome at the end of the A57 (page 4) . Had he continued via the M1, M25, M20, A20, E15, E17, E50, N19, E54 to Basel, over the Jungfrau, south at the Matterhorn, E27 to Torino, voila! A straight run into Roma.
Perhaps the proverb should be amended to 'All roads lead to Rome providing you don't stop at Worksop'.

**Peter Cubbin
Wallasey**

❏ Wives no longer feel any sense of duty to their husbands. When they take their marriage vows they promise to honour and obey you. But the moment you ask them to do a simple favour, like bring you a cake with a gun in it, they hand your letter to the prison authorities.

**P. Hammond-Organ
High security 'E' wing
HMP Durham**

❏ Women secretaries have no sense of loyalty to their employers. There're happy to cash their pay cheques, drink your coffee and use your phone, but the minute you try giving them a quick Christmas bonus behind the filing cabinet they go straight to the police.

**P. Hammond-Organ
HMP Parkhurst, I.O.W.**

We all pulled together in the old days

❏ I don't understand the youth of today with their drink, drugs and cigarette smoking. When I was a lad in the Boy Scouts all we had was communal masturbation, but we made do. Happy days indeed.

**Ian McKenzie
Woodwork teacher
Caithness**

❏ Richard bleeding Whitely off Countdown tried to scrounge directions to the nearest payphone off me as I stood outside RAF Leuchars, near Dundee, recently. I gave him thirty seconds to sling his fucking hook.

**Trev Hutton
Neston**

Frank Wanks... *Nationwide*

Hello. Frank Bough, here. Today, I'm having a wank in Richmond, North Yorkshire

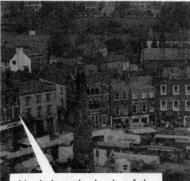

Nestled on the banks of the River Swale, Richmond...uh! ...uh! ...uh! ...Richmond is a town unlike any other.. ooh, yeah!..with It's cobbled streets and ancient uh!..oo ooohl.. market place

Richmond is also a town steeped in history. A history that lingers in... in..uh!.. uh!... uh! ..in it's narrow alleys.. uh! ..ooh, yes!.. yes!..yes!..and it's.quaint and beautiful buildings....... Christ, yeah!

In 1071, uh!...uh!...uh!...the Norman invaders built.. yeah!.. built a castle which today uh!.. uh!.. uh! ..today remains..uh!..uh!..uh!..only as a ruin.. uh!.. uh!..uh! uhluh!..yes.. yes.. YES...YES..YES.. **YES**........URRRRGH!

Phew! That's all for this week. See you next time

STARWATCH

MIRIAM'S PHOTO CASEBOOK

COME ON ANNE. WE'RE LOSING SALES! GET YOUR FUCKING KIT OFF WILL YOU!

YOU KNEW THE RULES WHEN YOU TOOK THE JOB.

MR MORGAN WAS VERY SPECIFIC. HE SAID THERE'D BE SEMI-NUDE PICTURES INVOLVED

WHAT WILL MY MUM THINK? SHE READS THE MIRROR

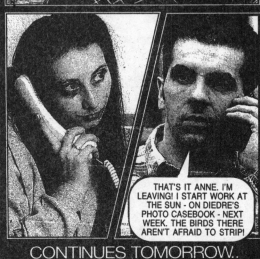

THAT'S IT ANNE. I'M LEAVING! I START WORK AT THE SUN - ON DIEDRE'S PHOTO CASEBOOK - NEXT WEEK. THE BIRDS THERE AREN'T AFRAID TO STRIP!

CONTINUES TOMORROW...

STARS in their TOILETS

❑ Next time brainy twat Jeremy Paxman starts bullying one of his Newsnight guests they should try asking him whether he washes his hands after he's used the toilet. I stood next to him at Paddington station toilets last year and he definitely did not. A smug swot he may be, but hygienic he isn't.

Lee Allberry
Evesham

❑ Whilst nipping into the gents at San Fransisco airport last summer I met Andy Bell from pop duo Erasure who fortunately was on his way out. I went in and had a good look around for Vince Clark before cautiously getting my knob out.

Andy D.
Leicester

❑ I syphoned the python next to Bryan Robson in a Manchester hotel during the 80s when he was out on the hoy with Kevin Moran, Paul McGrath and Norman Whiteside. I can't criticise his bladder capacity - he must have pissed about ten pints in one go - but his 'red (or purple) devil' was not what you'd expect from the captain of England.

Michael French
Sheldon, Birmingham

❑ I'm one of your growing army of young, trendy readers. I was in the merchant navy during the early sixties and met some Royal Navy boys who'd worked on Britannia. They hadn't shared a loo with the Royals, but they'd tampered with the plumbing and managed to catch one of Princess Margaret's dog eggs which they kept proudly displayed on a red cushion. By all accounts it made Bjork's gut strainer (issue 87) look like a chipolata.

H. A.
Littlehampton

TRANSVESTITES.
Disguise those big,
unfeminine feet by
dressing up as a female
clown.

T. Sheriff
Nottingham

APPEASE grumpy vicars
by sticking a length of
double sided Sellotape
along the hem of your
wedding dress. This will
automatically clean up
confetti from the church
floor as you walk down
the aisle.

Loggy
Hungerford

Top Tips

MAKE people think you
work in the zoo by going
to work wearing a wet
suit and carrying a
bucket of fish.

John Chant
e-mail

DETER lower-middle
class neighbours from
displaying signs in their
lavatory which say 'If
you sprinkle whilst you
tinkle, please be sweet
and wipe the seat' by
pissing on their tooth
brushes and shitting in
the bath every time you
see one.

Paul Browne
London SE13

MOTORISTS. At night
convince oncoming
drivers that the road has
'speed humps' by regu-
larly slowing to a virtual
stop and then flashing
your headlights.

J. Ryan
E mail

DETER goldfish from
having sex by throwing a
small bucket of air over
any that you catch in the
act.

W. T. Conqueror
Hastings

ALWAYS fart into the
rings on top of your gas
cooker. This will turn
back the gas meter, and
save you pounds over a
period of time.

C. Custer
Little Bighorn

Do you want to buy this cupboard? The door locks but there's no visible locking mechanism - only £5

There must be a catch

21

A unique collection any breakfast-lover will be proud to own

The Breakfast Heritage Showcase

To celebrate 500 years of breakfast cereals Silverfish & Woodlouse are proud to present the ultimate fine art collection - thirty magnificent hand-painted sculptures representing the world's most popular breakfast cereals.

Skilfully hand-crafted

The *Breakfast Heritage Showcase* is an important collection of life-size cereal sculptures by consummate food artist *Titus Domestos* to celebrate the quimcentenary of the first meal of the day. It captures for all time the whole malted goodness of the Shreddie, the sparkling gr-r-r-reatness of the Frostie, the snap, crackle and popness of the Rice Crispy, the dour in-edibility of the Special K, and the originality and bestness of the magnificent Corn Flake, the undisputed King of the Cereal Bowl.

A magnificent display cabinet at no extra cost

The *Breakfast Heritage Showcase* collector collection has its own specially designed genuine 'wood' style display cabinet**, a fitting home for your cereal collection. Suitable for wall hanging, free-standing or throwing in a skip, as a privileged collector you will receive this display stand absolutely FREE in return for a nominal purchase charge of £29.95 (at the time of going to press).

Detail of Shreddie

Detail of Cornflake

RESERVATION APPLICATION

: Silverfish and Woodlouse, Wainscoting House, Skirtingboard Way, Banbury.

ease accept my reservation for *The Breakfast Heritage Showcase*, a collection of nd crafted breakfast cereal sculptures. Every other month a pair of cereal gurettes will be sent to my home on approval, however I need only pay for one gure per week, at the bargain price of just £49.95 (plus £20 p+p). If I am not mpletely satisfied I may make fruitless attempts to cancel my subscription at any ne including writing a stream of hard luck letters to BBC's Watchdog which will rve only to amuse the programme researchers. My statutory rights are not portant.

ame _____

ddress _____

ease select your method of payment:

☐ Fifty pound note   ☐ Two twenties and a ten

e may occasionally (that is to say always and without exception) make your tails available to other companies who give us money in return for the names d addresses of gullible people like yourself. If you would prefer us not to do so, nply inform us in person at our offices in Banbury on any weekday morning tween 8.00 and 8.05am(closed Monday - Friday).

The Artist

Titus Domestos was born in 1955 on the Greek Island of Spatchulos, the son of a tortoise farmer. His father died when he was three, and Titus struggled to support his family sculpting models of elevenses biscuits out of driftwood and selling them to tourists. He absquatulated from the world renowned Ecole des Beaux Arts de Petits Dejeuners, Paris in 1976. He presently resides in Hove with his father, a retired fisherman.

*Due to the natural weathering properties of the materials used, the Fine Art Cereal Statuettes may appear to go soft and mouldy with time. This is a normal design feature and will add to the character and charm of the sculptures.

**The cabinet you receive will differ dramatically from that illustrated. Due to the flammable nature of the 'wood' style materials used, your display showcase should be mounted at least 2 metres away from any source of heat, radiators etc.

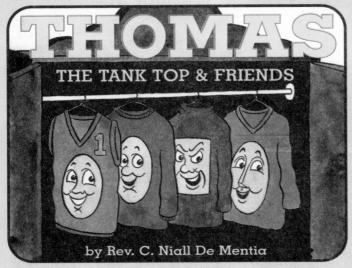

THOMAS
THE TANK TOP & FRIENDS

by Rev. C. Niall De Mentia

Thomas the Tank Top was twenty years old. His colours were fading, his collar was frayed and he'd started to bobble. But he was a very proud jumper and he thought himself the smartest garment in the wardrobe.

One morning, the Fat Cunt opened the wardrobe. "I am going to a party tonight", he announced. "I shall choose one of you to wear, so you must all be on your best behaviour. Now I'm going to have a shit and read the Express," he said importantly.

The pullovers were very excited. "Who do you think he will wear to the party?" asked Jamie the Red Jumper. "I hope it's me, I hope it's me," said Thomas knittedly. "Why would he choose **you**?" sneered Roland the Rollneck. "You haven't even got any sleeves."

"I've got a lovely snug neckline," he boasted. "I'm long and smart and I'm the height of fashion. What's more, I'm 98% Viscose." Roland the Rollneck was the newest jumper in the wardrobe, and the Fat Cunt wore him on all the important occasions.

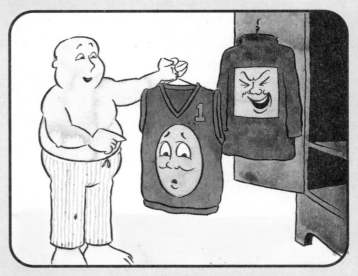

The Fat Cunt came back from his shit to get dressed. The Troublesome Trolleys had been up to their tricks again, jumping out of the laundry basket and missing the wash. "Oh, bother!" he grumbled. "Skid marks on my shreddies. Now I'll have an itchy crack all day."

"I'm going to do some gardening today and I don't want to get any of my nice jumpers messed up for the party," the Fat Cunt said. "So I'm going to wear you, Thomas." "Ha! Ha!" laughed Roland the Rollneck. "Have fun, Thomas. Try not to get **too** dirty."

All day long, the Fat Cunt worked in the garden, digging and hoeing and forking and weeding. Thomas the Tank Top was getting dirtier and dirtier. "Oh, poor old me! Oh, poor old me! What will I do? What will I do?" cried Thomas, textile-ishly.

Suddenly Thomas heard a voice. "I've been washed, especially for the party", said Roland. "Well, I'm working hard," replied Thomas. "The Fat Cunt might take me to the party to say 'thank you'." "Stuff and nonsense," replied the rude rollneck. "The only place he'll take you is a jumble sale".

That night, the Fat Cunt came to the wardrobe to announce his decision. "You have all been very good jumpers, but I can only wear one of you to the party," he said. "And I have chosen Roland the Rollneck." Thomas was very upset. "I said he'd pick me! I said he'd pick me!" chuffed Roland.

But when the Fat Cunt put Roland on, he got a big surprise. Roland no longer fitted! "You've fucking **shrank!**" he exclaimed. "That Fat Cow has put you in too hot a wash. I can't wear you ever again. From now on, Roland, I'll use you as a rag. You can go in the shed to clean my paint brushes."

"I'll need another jumper," he announced. "Thomas, as you have worked so hard all day, I'll wear you to the party, along with Clarrie and Annabel, my flared trousers." "Oh, good, sir! Oh, thank you, sir! I won't let you down, sir!" Thomas bobbled, acrylicly.

Thomas, Clarrie and Annabel looked magnificent under the disco lights as the Fat Cunt danced the night away. "Hey, I love your retro-chique gear," said a plump titted bird. "Fancy coming upstairs for a shag?" The Fat Cunt smiled. "Well done, Thomas," he said. "You're a Really Useful Jumper!"

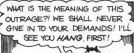

Spice of DEATH!

MOST girls would simply dread being dead. Turning up at your own funeral with your hair falling out and your eyeballs in an advanced state of putrification would be the ultimate fashion faux par.

But nowadays dying doesn't mean losing your looks - thanks to the rising popularity of TV morticians like McCallum and Silent Witness's Dr Samanda Burton.

Scud

To celebrate, erm... the continued popularity of the Spice Girls, and the new series of Silent Witness, we wondered whether sexy stiff surgeon Dr Sam *cadaver* go at giving the fab five a post mortem make-over. And of *corpse* she was only too happy to oblige.

Exocet

So what would be the first thing she'd do if the fab five turned up their toes and turned into Stiff Spices on her autopsy slab?

Patriot

Perhaps surprisingly her first priority would be to cut out their eyeballs.

"It may not sound like the most glamorous treatment but the results are fantastic". Dr Sam told us. "And the alternative is dreadful sunken eyes as the eyeballs collapse and shrivel up". After popping the unwanted peepers in the bin Dr Sam would then pack the empty eye sockets with cotton wool before closing the eyelids.

Trident

Next she would carefully bung up a cork up Scary, Sexy, Sporty, Posh and Baby's backsides to save the girl's the embarrassment of farting at their own funerals! "Believe it or not the Spice Girl's digestive systems will continue to work for some time after their death due to their bacterial nature. Unexpected anal announcements are fairly common among corpses".

Then comes the second facial treatment, ramming wax up the girl's noses to prevent their rotting brains slipping out at an inopportune moment.

Then Dr Sam would sew up their smackers, lovingly stitching the girls mouths closed before applying a delicate lip gloss.

Spam

Draining the girl's blood would the major treatment on the agenda. Dr Sam would do this by inserting a needle into their veins and forcing a stirrup pump up under the sternum and into the heart. The blood would then be replaced with formaldehyde.

Spam

Time now for a relaxing all over body massage, concentrating on the girl's finger tips and toes, to make sure the preservative fluid is properly distributed and reaches all the extremities.

Spam

When they died the Spice Girls could have been forgiven for thinking they'd had their last hair-do. But no. Their hair, as well as finger and toe nails, would

continue to grow for some time after their deaths. So sexy Dr Sam, who doubles as a stylist and beautician, would give the girls a cut and blow dry followed by a nice manicure.

Spam

The good news is that Dr Sam's gory surgical skills would not be required unless the Spice Girl's died in suspicious circumstances. If they did she would require her full tool kit to slice all five of them wide open from their chins to their coccyx, rend open their rib cages and remove their organs one at a time whilst talking into a Dictaphone. Inbetween autopsies she would no doubt stop and eat a sandwich.

Spam

Lastly, when the corpses were reassembled and dressed, Dr Sam would use her feminine fashion instincts to apply a loving touch of powder to bring much needed colour back to the fab five's faces.

Telly corpse cop quack gives fab five a mortuary make-over

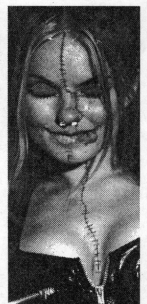

BEFORE and AFTER! Clockwise from bottom left, the Spice Girls alive yesterday (8 o'clock), sexy Dr Sam is ready for work (above right, about 1.30) and Sexy Spice looks stunning after her death mask facial (6.00pm, below)

5 things to do if you find a DEAD SPICE GIRL

Here's some tips from TV's sexiest detective death doc on what to do if you come across a Stiff Spice.

1. **Check her pulse to make sure she is deceased.**
2. **Draw a line round her with white chalk.**
3. **Carefully place any small objects that you find in a plastic freezer bag.**
4. **If there is a gun on the floor, bend down and pick it up slowly on the end of a pencil.**
5. **Smell it to see whether it has been fired recently.**

WIFE & 3 KIDS TO SUPPORT.

29

GILBERT RATCHET

(SIGH) I'VE FALLEN IN LOVE WITH THIS GIRL DOWN THE ROAD, READERS. HER NAME IS KYLIE POCAHONTAS BUZZLIGHTYEAR McDERMOT

I'M GOING TO IMPRESS KYLIE BY DOING HANDSTANDS IN FRONT OF HER HOUSE

IT'LL BE A DOODLE WITH THE AID OF THIS "HANDSTAND-O-MATIC" I'M BUILDING

THERE. PRETTY IMPRESSIVE HANDSTAND, EH KYLIE?

PERHAPS YOU'D DO ME THE HONOUR OF BEING MY GIRLFRIEND?

SORRY GILBERT — BUT THERE'S ONLY ONE WAY YOU CAN **REALLY** IMPRESS ME

AND THAT'S TO HAVE A GREAT BIG TATTOO DONE — ON **YOUR FACE**

AND SO... TATTOO-U-REGRET

CRIMMINEY! JUST LOOK AT THOSE PRICES

WHERE AM I GOING TO FIND FIFTY QUID TO GET A BIG TATTOO ON MY FACE?

HELLO — IT'S THE VICAR

GOOD AFTERNOON GILBERT

IT'S A BEAUTIFUL DAY AND LIFE IS GRAND, GILBERT — SO I DECIDED TO HAVE THIS TATTOOED ON MY BUTTOCK

GOD IS NICE

IT'S MY WAY OF THANKING THE LORD FOR THIS WONDERFUL WORLD WE LIVE IN

READ ALL ABOUT IT! LOADS OF PEOPLE ARE DYING, EVERYTHING'S SHIT AND NOW IT'S STARTING TO DRIZZLE

OH NO! IT LOOKS LIKE GOD ISN'T NICE AFTER ALL

HOW EMBARRASSING. NOW I'LL HAVE TO GET THIS TATTOO REMOVED

I CAN HELP YOU THERE, VICAR — FOR A SMALL FEE OF FIFTY QUID

JUST BEND OVER, AND I'LL ERASE YOUR TATTOO WITH MY PORTABLE ELECTRIC SANDER

FRRRRRRRR

JEEPERS CREEPERS

MY SANDER IS GOING THROUGH THE VICAR'S BUMCHEEK LIKE A KNIFE THROUGH BUTTER

WHY YOU CRETIN! YOU'VE SHREDDED MY BUTTOCK RIGHT DOWN TO THE BONE

YOU'LL NOT BE GETTING FIFTY QUID OUT OF ME

NEVER MIND. I'LL SIMPLY INVENT AN AUTOMATIC TATTOOING MACHINE WITH WHICH TO TATTOO MY OWN FACE

ALL I NEED IS A PNEUMATIC DRILL, A BOTTLE OF INK, AN OLD SEWING MACHINE — AND A BIT OF DO-IT-YOURSELF WIZARDRY

SHORTLY...

THIS WILL BE A VERY DELICATE OPERATION, READERS

THE NEEDLE MUST JUST PASS THROUGH THE TOP LAYER OF SKIN WITH HAIR'S-BREADTH PRECISION, SO THAT NONE OF THE SUBTLETIES OF THE TATTOO'S DESIGN WILL BE LOST

THUMPA THUMPA THUMPA

MASH MASH MASH

MASH MASH MASH

OOF OOF OOF

OOF OOF OOF

BAH! THIS STUPID MACHINE JUST GAVE ME A SORE HEAD

I'LL NEVER GET MY FACE TATTOOED AT THIS RATE

EXCUSE ME YOUNG MAN — I AM AN ECCENTRIC FIFTY-QUID-IONNAIRE, AND I COLLECT ALL THINGS WHICH COST FIFTY QUID

NOW. HOW MUCH DOES THAT MACHINE OF YOURS COST?

ERM...... FIFTY QUID?

I'LL BUY IT! HERE'S FIFTY QUID

AT THE TATTOO PARLOUR

HOORAY! NOW I CAN AFFORD A PROPER TATTOO

I'LL HAVE "ALL COPPERS ARE BASTARDS" IN BIG LETTERS ACROSS MY FOREHEAD PLEASE MISTER

I CAN HARDLY WAIT FOR KYLIE TO SEE THIS

SHE'LL PROBABLY BE OVERWHELMED WITH ADMIRATION FOR ME

ALAS BUT GILBERT, I MERELY WANTED AN IMPRESSIVE CEREMONIAL MILITARY DISPLAY OR PAGEANT TO BE PERFORMED ON THIS 4-FOOT BY 3-FOOT BLOWN-UP PHOTOGRAPH OF YOUR FEATURES

OH NO! SHE MEANT **THAT** SORT OF "BIG TATTOO ON MY FACE"

THEN THAT'S A STROKE OF LUCK!

THE ROYAL FULCHESTER FUSILIERS PRESENT

A GRAND MILITARY TATTOO TODAY AT THE PARK PARADE GROUND

COME ON KYLIE, LET'S GET OVER TO THE PARADE GROUND

SO FULCHESTER FUSILIERS PRESENT GRAND MILITARY TATTOO

OH GILBERT, I'LL BE SO IMPRESSED WHEN THEY START MARCHING ON YOUR FACE WITH THEIR DRUMS AND THAT

IT'LL MAKE ME WANT TO GO OUT WITH YOU LOADS

BUT... WE PROUDLY PRESENT THAT LITTLE BLOKE OFF 'FANTASY ISLAND', IN A TANK

BOSS! BOSS! THE PLANE! THE PLANE!

OH NO! IT'S **THAT** SORT OF "MILITARY TATTOO"

READERS VOICE: OH NO! IT'S THAT SORT OF "CARTOON ENDING" AGAIN.

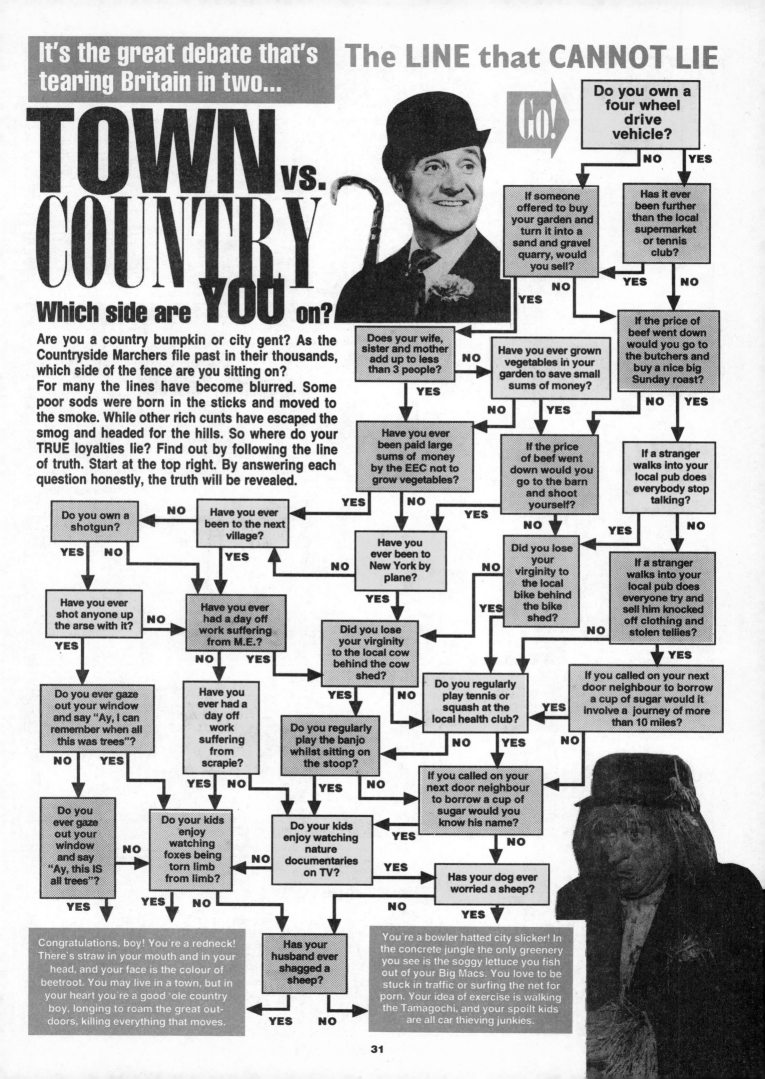

It's the great debate that's tearing Britain in two...

The LINE that CANNOT LIE

TOWN VS. COUNTRY?

Which side are YOU on?

Are you a country bumpkin or city gent? As the Countryside Marchers file past in their thousands, which side of the fence are you sitting on?

For many the lines have become blurred. Some poor sods were born in the sticks and moved to the smoke. While other rich cunts have escaped the smog and headed for the hills. So where do your TRUE loyalties lie? Find out by following the line of truth. Start at the top right. By answering each question honestly, the truth will be revealed.

Go!

Do you own a four wheel drive vehicle?

NO / YES

If someone offered to buy your garden and turn it into a sand and gravel quarry, would you sell?

Has it ever been further than the local supermarket or tennis club?

YES / NO

NO

YES

Does your wife, sister and mother add up to less than 3 people?

NO

Have you ever grown vegetables in your garden to save small sums of money?

If the price of beef went down would you go to the butchers and buy a nice big Sunday roast?

NO / YES

YES

NO / YES

Have you ever been paid large sums of money by the EEC not to grow vegetables?

If the price of beef went down would you go to the barn and shoot yourself?

If a stranger walks into your local pub does everybody stop talking?

YES / NO

YES

NO

YES

Do you own a shotgun?

NO

Have you ever been to the next village?

YES

Have you ever been to New York by plane?

NO

Did you lose your virginity to the local bike behind the bike shed?

YES

If a stranger walks into your local pub does everyone try and sell him knocked off clothing and stolen tellies?

YES / NO

YES

NO

YES

Have you ever shot anyone up the arse with it?

NO

Have you ever had a day off work suffering from M.E.?

YES

Did you lose your virginity to the local cow behind the cow shed?

NO

Do you regularly play tennis or squash at the local health club?

YES

If you called on your next door neighbour to borrow a cup of sugar would it involve a journey of more than 10 miles?

YES

NO

YES / NO

Do you ever gaze out your window and say "Ay, I can remember when all this was trees"?

NO / YES

Have you ever had a day off work suffering from scrapie?

YES / NO

Do you regularly play the banjo whilst sitting on the stoop?

YES / NO

NO / YES

NO

If you called on your next door neighbour to borrow a cup of sugar would you know his name?

YES

NO

Do you ever gaze out your window and say "Ay, this IS all trees"?

NO

Do your kids enjoy watching foxes being torn limb from limb?

NO

Do your kids enjoy watching nature documentaries on TV?

YES

Has your dog ever worried a sheep?

YES

YES / NO

YES

Congratulations, boy! You're a redneck! There's straw in your mouth and in your head, and your face is the colour of beetroot. You may live in a town, but in your heart you're a good 'ole country boy, longing to roam the great out-doors, killing everything that moves.

Has your husband ever shagged a sheep?

YES / NO

You're a bowler hatted city slicker! In the concrete jungle the only greenery you see is the soggy lettuce you fish out of your Big Macs. You love to be stuck in traffic or surfing the net for porn. Your idea of exercise is walking the Tamagochi, and your spoilt kids are all car thieving junkies.

31

FARMER PALMER

SHEP! SHEP! COME BY LAD! COME BY!

WHEE-EEP! WHEE-EEP!

HUP! HUP! GOOD LAD! COME BY!

GOOD BOY SHEP.

BANG!

LATER...

AH! PALMER!

HOW CAPITAL TO SEE YOU WHAT-WHAT - AND THIS MUST BE YOUR LAD JETHRO?

OOH AAR SQUOYRE

WHAT-WHAT JETHRO.

WE BE LEAVIN' I22 BRAIN FALLOW THIZ YURR ZURR.

ANYWAY PALMER, I HOPE YOU'LL BE COMING UP TO LONDON FOR THE COUNTRYSIDE MARCH WHAT-WHAT.

OOH AAR YURR LORDSHIB.

BECAUSE, YOU SEE, YOUR WAY OF LIFE IS UNDER THREAT...

BECAUSE, IF YOU DON'T GO ON THE MARCH, I'LL THROW YOU OUT OF YOUR COTTAGE.

AS I WAS SAYING TO SOME OF THE CHAPS ON THE COCOA FUTURES DESK - WE COUNTRY PEOPLE WILL NOT BE TOLD WHAT TO DO BY TOWNIES AND OUTCOMERS.

OOH AAR.

AS YOU KNOW, PALMER, IT IS DIFFICULT FOR ME TO SPEND AS MUCH TIME AS I WOULD LIKE IN THE COUNTRY.

THIS IS UNFORTUNATELY UNAVOIDABLE - AS MY HOME AND INTERESTS ARE IN LONDON.

BUT IT REALLY IS DREADFUL. EVERY TIME I COME HERE I SEE MORE OF THESE OIKS - DEMANDING THE RIGHT TO ROAM OVER MY COUNTRYSIDE.

WHAT THEY DON'T REALISE IS THAT BY PREVENTING THEM TRAMPING ALL OVER IT, I'M SAFEGUARDING OUR HERITAGE FOR FUTURE GENERATIONS...

ROYT YOOZ I222.

SO THAT THEIR CHILDREN, THEIR CHILDRENS CHILDREN AND THEIR CHILDREN'S CHILDREN WON'T BE ALLOWED TO GO ON IT EITHER.

THEY SAY THEY UNDERSTAND THE COUNTRYSIDE - BUT I BET THEY WOULDN'T EVEN KNOW WHAT A...A...A... SHOOTING STICK WAS!

LET ALONE HOW TO LOAD AND FIRE ONE.

AND THERE'S ANOTHER THING - FOXES...!

BLEEP! BLEEP!

EXCUSE ME - I'VE GOT AN E-MAIL COMING THROUGH ON MY PSION.

WHAT'S THAT, RUPERT? HORLICKS UP SIX AGAINST A BASKET OF COCOA?

SELL TO OPEN! I'LL BE THERE AS QUICK AS I CAN. I'M IN THE BACK OF FACKING BEYOND AT THE MOMENT.

I'VE GOT TO 'COPTER BACK TO LONDON. SEE YOU THERE ON SATURDAY, PALMER.

WHAT WHAT

SO...

LIKE INCEST, HOSTILITY, SUICIDE

AND BESTIALITY.

HANDS OFF OUR COUNTRY

LIZZEN TO U22

R.M.S. *SHITE-ANIC*

Really Massive Shite discovered on sea bed

THE gigantic last stool ever moved by the captain of the Titanic has been discovered lying intact two and a half miles beneath the Atlantic ocean.

The giant dog's egg is thought to have been laid by Captain Smith on the night the ill fated liner sank. Eye witnesses reported seeing the captain shit his pants as the Titanic collided with an enormous iceberg, and several survivors spoke of eerie farting noises and unpleasant smells as the ship went down. But until now the sea has refused to give up any faecal evidence to support these claims.

Scientists

Now scientists believe they have located the world's most famous dog's egg. And remarkably enough it appears to have been almost perfectly preserved despite being buried at sea for an amazing 86 years.

Dogs

"The Richard is lying in one piece, still perfectly

Conway - Shitty obsession has cost him dearly.

curled and crimped", said sub mariner Russ Conway who made the discovery in his specially designed underwater exploration vessel China Tea. "It is a quite awesome sight. To look at it you would think it was fresh - as if had only just been nipped off yesterday".

Most organic matter would decay rapidly in sea water, however scientists believe the reason for the turd's remarkable preservation is quite straightforward. "Fortunately for us fish wouldn't touch it with a barge poll", Conway told us. "It has literally remained untouched for all this time".

Axemen

In 1987 Conway, 71, gave up a successful career as a pianist to concentrate on his life-long search for the turd. It's an obsession which has cost him dear. His wife of 17 years, sour faced pseudo intellectual singer Tinita Tikarum left him in 1995, and Conway

Conway aboard his exploration vessel 'Limbo' yesterday

has run up debts of over £2 million financing underwater searches. But now at last his dedication appears to have paid off.

There are ambitious plans to raise the shi-tanic and put it on permanent display as a floating exhibit, probably somewhere like

---

SHITWRECKED *The stinking of the Titanic*

It was approaching midnight on Sunday 14th of April 1912. The RMS Titanic was midway through her maiden voyage from Southampton to New York. Their was a party atmosphere on board as the passengers relaxed following their evening meal.

After a particularly heavy dinner Captain Smith told fellow officers that he was going down below to curl one off, leaving First Officer Murdoch in charge of the bridge. The sea was calm, but it was a dark, cold, moonless night.

Iceberg

Up in the crow's nest lookout Frederick Fleet spotted a giant black silhouette looming directly ahead of the ship.
"Iceberg dead ahead!" he cried.

Fleet - spotted iceberg from crow's nest.

Realising the danger First Officer Murdoch gave the immediate order "Full

Murdoch - left in charge of bridge.

speed astern and hard a's-tarboard" in the vein hope of avoiding a collision.

Cos

Meanwhile in the officer's toilets Captain Smith was sitting down with a copy of the Picture Post. He had already got the turtle's

head, but he had been egg bound since leaving Southampton and he knew that a long and difficult shite lay ahead. But a sudden judder as the ship's engines went into reverse told him something was wrong. He leapt to his feet, pulled up his trousers and returned to the bridge, arriving just in time to see the enormous iceberg towering above the bow of his vessel.

Rocket

"Fuck me!" he cried in horror. There was a sudden rumble in his trousers. Captain Smith was an experienced sailor - indeed this was to have been his final voyage before retirement - but no man on Earth could have regulated his bowel in

'Amidst the farting and screaming Captain Smith realised that the follow through was unavoidable'

such dire circumstances. A series of eerie, juddering farts echoed around the ship as his rectum began to slowly and involuntarily relax.

36

How they found the turd of the Titanic

Hartlepool. But at least one shit scientist believes there would be enormous risks involved. Professor Karl Heinz-Bigsoup of the Tampa Bay University of Faeces believes that the massive log will be unstable.

Plank Spankers

"Even after 86 years there is still a high risk that it will be minging. And the chances of raising it from the sea bed without anyone getting shit behind their fingernails are remote".

Tub Thumpers

There has been mixed reaction to news of the discovery. Captain Smith's daughter, TV chef Delia, believes her dad's stool should left to rest in peace. "This huge underwater crap is a sea grave. Perhaps they could stick a lollipop stick in it with a little inscription or something. But apart from that I think they should leave it alone", she said yesterday.

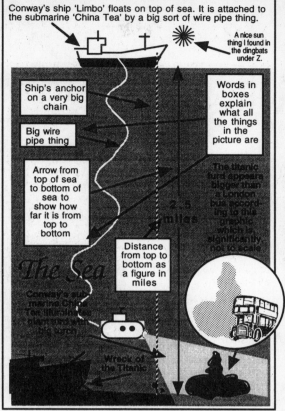

Conway's ship 'Limbo' floats on top of sea. It is attached to the submarine 'China Tea' by a big sort of wire pipe thing.

A nice sun thing I found in the dingbats under Z.

Ship's anchor on a very big chain

Big wire pipe thing

Arrow from top of sea to bottom of sea to show how far it is from top to bottom

Words in boxes explain what all the things in the picture are

The titanic turd appears bigger than a London bus according to this graphic which is significantly not to scale

2.5 miles

Distance from top to bottom as a figure in miles

The Sea

Conway's submarine China Tea illuminates giant turd with big torch.

Wreck of the Titanic

☐ Graphic by some geeky little anorak on a computer

Giz a jobbie!

'Giz a job' actor Bernard Hill who played Captain Smith in the blockbuster Hollywood movie gasped in horror when we showed him pictures of the Captain's gigantic brown trout.

"I definitely *couldn't* do dat", quipped the former Boy from the Black Stuff.

Film makers have been accused of distorting the truth by omitting any reference to the Captain shitting his self from the movie script. Contrary to events featured in the film, surviving witnesses recall passengers jumping overboard to avoid the smell.

"It was nothing like the movie", said 28 year old Ann McMahon who lost her mother on that fateful night. "The stench of rotten cabbage was unbearable", she recalled. "All the people who were drowning came up to the surface, took one whiff and decided to go straight back down again."

Asked what he would have done if he had been the real captain of the Titanic, Hill said he'd have put the vessel in reverse.

"I'd have sailed back to the iceberg and everyone could have climbed off onto that".

Titanic (above) sets sail and Smith (below) who laid the monster cable.

Amidst the farting and screaming Captain Smith realised that the follow through was unavoidable. Within seconds he was touching cloth, and panic slowly began to spread around the upper decks. A sickly, pungent smell filled the cold night air and both passengers and crew held their noses or wafted frantically with their hands to avoid the hideous odour.

Banger

The Captain knew that if he lit a bum cigar on the bridge the consequences would be disastrous.

Selflessly he clambered down to the lower deck, pebble dashing several lifeboats as he went, and lowered his shit locker over the side. Witnesses recalled the purple faced captain grimacing as his mudhole expanded and a giant brown trout curled itself down into the water with an enormous splash. So heavy was the Captain's log that as it slid beneath the waves the ship rose several feet in the water.

Sparkler

Captain Smith's desperate final farts were clearly smelled on board the steam ship California only a few miles away. But the pong was so noxious her captain ordered matches be lit on deck, and he steered a course directly away from the Titanic at full speed. By 4.00am when the Carpathia finally arrived at the scene of the stinking all that remained were a few dangleberries bobbing about in the water.

DIARY of DISASTER

April 9th 1912
Captain complains of constipation after eating three Scotch Eggs and an omelette for lunch.

April 10th
Titanic sets sail from Southampton.
2.30pm - A passenger recalls seeing the Captain eating a large bag of bonfire toffee on the bridge.

April 11th
Despite continuing lack of bowel movement Captain orders two boiled eggs for breakfast and has egg fried rice for lunch.

April 14th
7.30am - Captain makes the fatal decision to have prunes for breakfast.
1.00pm - Beans on toast for lunch, followed by bread pudding. During the afternoon Captain ignores repeated warnings from his stomach about possible stool movement ahead.
7.00pm - Captain Smith dines with Mr and Mrs Arthur Askey, ordering cabbage soup, crab sticks, mince and dumplings followed by Death by Chocolate.
11.25pm - Captain retires to lavatory complaining of stomach cramps.
11.30pm - Look out reports iceberg dead ahead. Captain shits his pants.
2.30am - Going, going, pong. Titanic finally sinks.

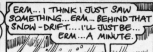

SHIRKER BEE

K-CHUNG!

WHAT BLOODY TIME D'YOU CALL THIS, ATKINS? YOU'RE FORTY MINUTES LATE!

YEAH... ERM... IT WAS ME MUM'S FUNERAL, SEE. SHE WAS CHEWED BY A BULLDOG. CAME AS A TERRIBLE SHOCK TO ALL OF US...

SNIFF

OH... RIGHT... WELL, I'M SORRY TO HEAR THAT ATKINS - AND ON BEHALF OF THE COMPANY I'D LIKE TO EXPRESS OUR SINCEREST...

HEH-HEH

OI! HOLD ON! YOU'RE A FUCKIN' BEE! WE'VE ALL GOT THE SAME MUM...

HER!!

I'M WARNING YOU, ATKINS. IF YOU'RE LATE ONCE MORE THIS WEEK, YOU'LL BE COLLECTING YOUR BEE-45, D'YOU HEAR ME?

'ERE - WHERE D'YOU THINK YOU'RE OFF TO NOW? YOU SHOULD'VE BEEN STACKING GRUBS IN THE NURSERY A BLOODY HOUR SINCE!

KEEP YER ANTENNAE ON.

I'M ANSWERING A CALL OF NATURE.

½ AN HOUR LATER...

WHAT THE HELL ARE YOU DOING IN THERE, ATKINS?

IF YOU'RE NOT OUT OF THERE IN TEN SECONDS, I'LL...

NOW WASH YOUR HALTAIRES

♪ DDDRRRINGG!! ♪

FLUSH!

SORRY BOSS. CAN'T TALK NOW.

TEA BREAK.

'OW D'YOU LIKE YOUR TEA, LUV?

MILK AND TWO NECTARS PLEASE.

'ERE DAVE. LOOK AT THE SPIRACLES ON THAT.

WE WERE UP ALL NIGHT WITH THE KIDS. THEY'RE GOING THROUGH THAT DIFFICULT LARVAL STAGE.

PHWOOAR!

DDRRINGG!!

THAT MEANS YOU AN' ALL, ATKINS. BACK TO WORK. DIDN'T YOU HEAR THE BELL?

BELL? WHAT BELL?

I CAN'T HEAR NOWT THESE DAYS. ITS ALL THIS BUZZING. IT'S DOIN' MY EARS IN. MY MATE SAYS I'M DUE TO SOME COMPENSATION.

THOUSANDS HE RECKONS.

LESS OF YOUR LIP, ATKINS. YOU'RE EMPLOYED HERE TO DO A JOB. NOW GET OVER THERE AND DO ONE OF THEM DANCES TO TELL THE REPS WHERE THERE'S LOADS OF POLLEN.

SORRY CHIEF. NO CAN DO.

YOU BLOODY WHAT?

NOT IN MY JOB DESCRIPTION, SEE. MY CONTRACT CLEARLY STATES THAT I AM EMPLOYED "TO PLACE WAX CAPS ON CELLS TO ENABLE THE LARVAE INSIDE TO SPIN A SILKEN COCOON AND PUPATE".

NOTHING THERE ABOUT DANCING.

IF YOU WANT A DANCE DOING - Y'CAN FUCKIN' DO IT YOURSELF. WHAT D'YOU THINK I AM - A DRONE?

WHERE ARE YOU GOING NOW?

BACK TO THE BOGS. THAT TEA'S GONE RIGHT THROUGH ME.

QUICK EVERYONE! WE'RE BEING SMOKED OUT! MAKE YOUR WAY TO THE DESIGNATED EXITS IN A CALM AND ORDERLY FASHION BEFORE YOU BECOME DROWSY AND NON-AGGRESSIVE. QUEENS AND PUPAE FIRST.

DINGALINGALING!

COUGH! COUGH!

SHORTLY...

RIGHT *COUGH*...IS EVERYBODY ACCOUNTED FOR?

ERM...EVERYBODY EXCEPT ONE... ATKINS.

ASSEMBLY POINT

DOH! I MIGHT OF KNOWN.

IT'S ALRIGHT, WE'VE FOUND HIM! HE WAS REVOLVING ON HIS BACK IN THE KHAZI.

ATKINS! ATKINS! ARE YOU ALRIGHT?

ALRIGHT? ALRIGHT?! OF COURSE I'M NOT FUCKIN' ALRIGHT. THIS HAS GOT TO BE WORTH AT LEAST TWO MONTHS OFF.

...ON FULL PAY.

Jack Black
& the Mystery of
Nicebury-on-the-Water

Jack Black and his dog Silver are staying with Aunt Meg at her beautiful home in the picturesque and unspoilt Cotswold village of Nicebury-on-the-Water.

What a really nice village this is, Aunt Meg. Quite idyllic - the sort of place Prince Charles would like.

Yes, Jack.

This is our little unspoilt corner of England. It has been like this for hundreds of years.

I've dusted all your lovely belongings Aunt Meg, and hoovered your nice carpets. Will that be all?

Yes, we'll see you tomorrow, Mrs P.

That's odd Silver. Mrs P the cleaner is going home on foot.

That afternoon, Jack took Silver for a walk in the village...

Well, if it isn't our mysterious cleaning lady. And it looks like she's been doing some shopping.

After Mrs P had gone, Jack and Silver went to investigate.

Woof! Woof!

What's that you've found, Silver?

Litter, in a lovely village like this. I don't believe it...

Hmmm. It's some sort of ticket.

Something isn't right here Silver, and I intend to get to the bottom of it!

The next morning.

I've got a W.I. meeting this morning Jack. Colonel Bagshott is giving a talk on bayonet techniques.

Mrs P the cleaner will be here any moment...

When she arrives could you ask her to plump up those two cushions.

No problem Aunt Meg. I'll tell her.

And the vase on the mantelpiece needs moving an inch to the left. She forget to do it yesterday.

The moment Aunt Meg was out of the house the young detective went to work...

Come on Silver. Let's make a giant pot of tea!

Shortly...

This is a nice surprise Jack! A lovely cup of tea before I start work.

Would you like some more?

I shouldn't really Jack. I've already had four cups.

No, please, do have a top up.

Later, not long after Mrs P had started her work...

Is it alright if I nip into the lavvy Jack?..

That tea has gone straight through me.

Really Mrs P, I don't think that would be very appropriate, do you?

Aunt Meg's lavatory is nice. Hadn't you better use your own?

I'm sorry about this Jack. I shouldn't have drank so much tea. I'll be back in ten minutes, as soon as I've used the lav.

But as soon as Mrs P had left, Jack and Silver dashed out the back door.

Come on Silver, no time to lose! We'll catch up with her at the end of the lane.

Woof! Woof!

There she is! Come on Silver, we mustn't lose her.

SPOILT BASTARD

LETTERBOCKS98

THE OFFICIAL SHITE LETTERS PAGE OF THE WORLD CUP 1998

My wife is mentally ill

❏ The other day my wife suggested we have my mother for tea on Mothering Sunday. Imagine my surprise when I came in from the pub to find my mother on a plate in the middle of the table, roasted and surrounded by vegetables.

Mr Pants
Oakworth, Keighley

❏ Is anyone else as pissed off as I am about the famous acting McGann brothers? There must be about fifty of them, and every one is a fanny rat. No wonder blokes like me can't get a girlfriend.

Mike Pearson
Leicester

A gorgeous McGann brother yesterday.

❏ They say that in this world you don't get anything for nothing. Tell that to the cunt who nicked my giro.

Chez
Sheffield

❏ Following on from Doc Cox's performance in issue 89. Rude vegetables are getting a lot ruder nowadays, I can tell you. I enclose a photo I took in my garden recently showing a pair of root vegetables engaged in apparent 'Golden Shower' shenanigans.

John Tait
Thropton

Letterbocks
PO Box 1PT
Newcastle upon Tyne
NE99 1PT
Fax: 0191 2414244
viz.comic@virgin.net

You must be skidding

❏ On that Continental tyres advert where the stuntman is skidding around on top of a skyscraper, why is he wearing a crash helmet? I didn't notice, but I bet he's wearing his seat belt too. What's the fucking point? The only sensible safety precaution in the circumstances would be rubber pants.

Jim Wood
Isle of Arran

❏ Why do they bother with soft porn? People that hate porn don't like it, and people that love porn don't like it. So what's the point?

Sasha Shaw
E mail

❏ I've always known that the Boat Race was contested by two teams of wankers, but its gratifying to see that the BBC have now recognised the fact.

~~weather.~~
12.00 Grandstand. 12.02 Boat Race Toss. 12.05 F Focus. 12.30 News. 12.35.The University B Race. 1.50 Racing from Newbury

"Every letter wins a goldfish"
That's the Letterbocks Goldfish Guarantee

❏ Tramps outside railway stations would do well to remember that 'honesty pays'. So stop asking people for "50p for a cup of tea". Why not come clean and ask for "£2 for a can of Special Brew"? I'd gladly cough up. In fact I might even join you for one.

Chris Mappley
Carshalton

❏ 'Neither a borrower nor a lender be' wrote William Shakespeare, the famed Bard of Avon. Well I'm the chief executive of one of Britain's largest banks, and we borrow about £50 million from the money markets each year, and lend out almost as much again. The bank makes in excess of £500 million profit each year, and I get paid around £1.5 million plus bonuses worth twice as much again.
All of which leaves Shakespeare looking a bit of a twat.

Martin Taylor
Threadneedle Street
London

❏ As I was preparing to put all my clocks forward one hour it suddenly occurred to me that they all go back again in October, so what is the point? Instead, to save all the fuss and confusion, I simply went through my diary putting all my engagements forward one hour during the summer months.
If everyone else was as practical as me we wouldn't need Moira Stewart to keep telling us twice a year to change the clocks, and people wouldn't need to shout at their wives for not being able to change the timer on the video.

D. Bradley
Shiremoor, Newcastle

Spud-U-look like

❏ Regarding your item on interestingly shaped vegetables. I've got a potato that looks like Alice Beer off Watchdog. Do I win £5?

Phil Crouch
Bourne, Lincs.
P.S. Come to think of it, I've got a whole sack of potatoes that look like Alice Beer off Watchdog. And a lemon.

Fruit cock and bull tail

❏ I am familiar with the recent phenomenon of Allah sending messages in tomatoes, however I was quite taken aback the other day when I received a message from the Easter Bunny inside a kumquat. I promptly replied - via a pomegranate - requesting a Chocolate Buttons Easter egg. To date it has not arrived, but my faith remains strong and I look forward to receiving it in the near future.

Galia Lunn
Huddersfield

❏ Have the ad men responsible for the Caffreys slogan "Strong words, softly spoken" never been to an Irish bar? Surely "Strong words, shouted incoherently" would be more appropriate.

J. Thompson
Cambridge

❏ I was fortunate enough to stand next to Meatloaf in the pisser at Cohuna National Park in Perth, the day after his concert in Bindoon, Western Australia in 1991. Outside, my wife was desperate to know how big his cock was.
Meat loaf? I've seen more meat in a Linda McCartney sausage roll.

Ray Galloway
e-mail

Puffa puffa mice

❏ Now that scientists have developed an apparent cure for cancer which has been used successfully on mice, isn't it about time the tobacco companies launched mice cigarettes? The potential worldwide market must be enormous.

S.T.
Chipboard-on-Tyne

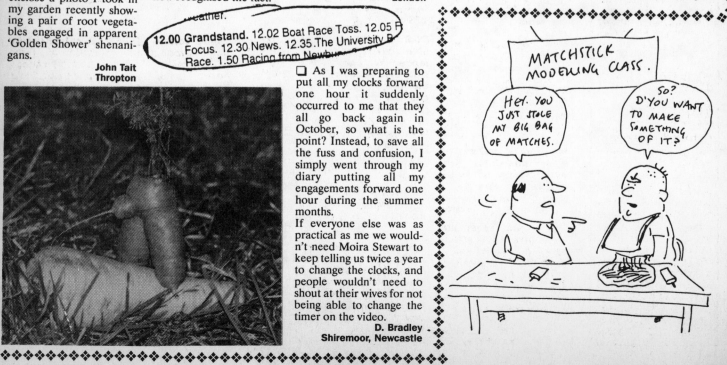

MATCHSTICK MODELLING CLASS.

HEY. YOU JUST STOLE MY BIG BAG OF MATCHES.

SO? D'YOU WANT TO MAKE SOMETHING OF IT?

PRISONER
of the
MONTH

* In every issue we give 3 convicts the chance to prove that they are interesting enough to deserve a pen friend. You can write to the interesting prisoners at the addresses below, but please do not send them any cakes as these are banned by the prison authorities.

Doing birds to doing bird

❑ At 18 I managed a top House club, then organised illegal raves before I fled to Spain and became a stripper which led to a career in porno movies. Later I set up my own nightclub, bar then brothel. There's a few stories I could tell you, I can tell you. Especially from my porno movie star period.
**RM1640 Lopez
HM Prison, North Square,
Dorchester DT1 1JD**

❑ My name is Norman. (Don't laugh cos I know you are doing). I'm 21 and love computers and reading. I've had tea with Bob Champion (the horse rider) and my schoolteacher kept a tiger as a pet. I believe him cos I've seen the photo.
**N. Pennington RP2897
F unit, HMP Wolds Prison,
Brough, HU15 2JZ**

Multi-coloured scrot shot

❑ I'm Keith, 31, from Hull, and I've been dumped by my ex partner. I once scratched my bollocks in the background on SwapShop and my mum once worked in the bar at Hull theatre and served a gin and tonic to Roger Lloyd-Pack, who asked her to have one herself.
**K. Parker BA6404
Wing B1-07, HM Prison
Hull, HU9 5LS**

Royal rumpus over labour plans to 'drown Queen in a bucket'

A SECRET Government document outlining radical proposals to cut the growing cost of maintaining the Royal Family has been made up by this newspaper.

A committee of leading Labour MPs formed in June to focus on the problem of feeding the growing number of Royals. Their brief was to look at alternative methods by which the Royal Family could be disposed of.

Storm

And one plan which is certain to create a storm of controversy is that the entire Royal Family should be drowned in a bucket of water.

Thighs

That drastic solution was the brainchild of New Labour spin doctor Peter Mandellson. And in a leaked memo to cabinet colleagues he emphasised the need to tread carefully in terms of public relations.

Clap

After drowning the Royals and burying them in a sack, he recommended that the public be 'misinformed' about their whereabouts.
'A highly emotional public reaction could perhaps be avoided if an official statement was released saying that the Royal

Mandellson's leaked menu sparks fury

Family had gone to live on a farm in Wales', Mandellson wrote in a letter to colleagues dated 10th October 1997.

Herpes

Yesterday public reaction to the leaked documents was mixed.
"How could anyone drown such lovely people?" said Mrs B. of Essex. "I think they're marvellous, they do a wonderful job". But one man from Ashington in Northumberland was in favour of having them killed, and even went as far as offering to do the job himself.

Hisbeans

"I'd kill them with a hammer in my back yard for two quid each", he told us. "Mind you, if I didn't get them first time I'd have to be quick on my feet. Once you've thumped them,

Mandellson - bucket

they don't half get angry".
Other schemes proposed in the controversial discussion document include giving the Royals injections that would make them go to sleep, or putting something in their milk. However left wing Labour MP Dennis Skinner, normally a thorn in the side of the Royals, was surprisingly AGAINST plans to have them put down.

Hasbeens

'I can't see why we shouldn't just have them neutered, then retire them to a field somewhere to live the rest of their lives in peace', we made him up as having said.

TOP TiPS

WHY pay £100 for a skip? Buy a clapped out, untaxed car for £25 and fill it with all your shite. Then sit back and wait for the authorities to tow it away.
*Ginga
The Wirral*

AN EMPTY aluminium cigar tube filled with angry wasps makes an inexpensive vibrator.
*Sister S. Berwick
Blackrod*

OLD FOLK. Never put more than £3 worth of petrol in your car at a time. You could pop your clogs at any moment, and you don't want some spawny relative copping for a free tankfull.
*Michael Jenkins
Bangor, Gwynedd*

DOG LOVERS. Catch a bluebottle after it has landed on your dog's shit, then preserve it in the fridge inside a jelly cube. If your dog dies the vet will then be able to recreate it using 'Jurassic Park' type DNA technology.
*J. Talt
Thropton*

FATTIES. Avoid eating between meals by simply allowing yourself 20 meals per day.
*A. Kettle
Kettering*

TERRIFY ants into believing they have been invaded by 'War Of The Worlds' style Martians by standing 3 pin plugs on end around their holes.
*J. T.
Thropton*

MIX Gold Blend coffee granules with bicarbonate of soda. Hey presto! Coffee flavoured 'space dust'.
*Henry Cordy
E mail*

CERTAIN types of lamp shades might make perfect party dresses for small Daleks.
*James Hinchcliffe
Manchester*

RICHARD Branson. Instead of wasting time and money chasing balloons across the desert, why not employ a few more people to answer the bloody phone when people are trying to book a seat on one of your bloody awful trains?
*W. E. Walker
Holme, Lancs.*

TAPE a chocolate bar to the outside of your microwave. If the chocolate melts you will know that microwaves are escaping and it is time to have the oven serviced.
*Terry Odgers
South Africa*

CAR cigarette lighters make ideal mini 'High Chaparral' style branding irons.
*JT
Thropton*

A LIGHT dusting of flour makes ideal 'snow on the track' for OO scale railway modellers who can't be arsed to run their train set on time this winter.
*A. Bond
London SE7*

ROBBIE RICKERBY
high-pressure salesman

EXCELLENT LEFTIE.

NO ROZZERS ARE GONNA GIVE US NO TROUBLE 'ROUND THESE PARTS.

THIS IS BRITAINS MOST REMOTEST BUILDING, IT'S 200 MILES FROM THE CLOSEST HOUSE AND 20 MILES FROM THE NEAREST PASSABLE DIRT TRACK.

WE CAN HOLE UP HERE 'TILL THE HEAT'S ORF.

LOOT

DING! DONG!

UH?!

LOOT

SHIT! D'YOU FINK WE'VE BEEN RUMBLED?

TUG!

YOU GO TO THE DOOR, AND YOU SEND WHOEVER IT IS PACKING, DO YOU UNDERSTAND?

YES.

REMEMBER WE'VE GOT YOUR WIFE HERE, PAL ....

WHATEVER YOU DO... DON'T LET THEM IN ... JUST GET RID!

OKAY. OKAY.

H... H... HEL... HEL... HELLO?

WELL, I WON'T KEEP YOU. I CAN SEE YOU'RE BEING HELD HOSTAGE BY TWO DESPERATE CRIMINALS, SO I'LL BE BRIEF WE WERE JUST IN THE AREA AND THIS IS ONLY A COURTESY CALL. YOU ARE, OF COURSE, UNDER NO OBLIGATION TO ADMIT ME TO YOUR PREMESIS, AND I CAN ASSURE YOU I'M NOT GOING TO TRY TO SELL YOU ANYTHING.

LOVELY COTTAGE THIS, IT'S GOT CHARACTER, THAT'S THE BEAUTY OF YOUR OLDER PROPERTIES ISN'T IT, CHARACHTER. MIND YOU, HAVING SAID THAT, I'LL BET IT GETS DRAUGHTY ON THE WINTER NIGHTS, ESPECIALLY IN SUCH AN EXPOSED POSTION.

SHAT-AP!

I RECKON YOU'D SEE THIS PLACE DOUBLE GLAZED, U.P.V.C. FRAMES IN WHITE OR TRADITIONAL WOOD EFFECT FOR EIGHT THOUSAND POUNDS, FULLY FITTED, ALL IN.

SHUT UP FOR GOD'S SAKE!

TELL YOU WHAT. I'LL RING MY BOSS. Y'SEE I NEED AUTHORISATION TO GO BELOW EIGHT THOUSAND.

YES... RIGHT... YES... YES... RIGHT... YEP. YEP... OKAY.

IT'S YOUR LUCKY DAY. THE BOSS SAYS HE CAN CLEAR ME TO GO AS LOW AS SIX THOUSAND.

UH?! WE CUT THE PHONE LINES THIS MORNIN'!

LISTEN. I TELL YOU WHAT. I'LL GO OVER HIS HEAD. I'LL DO IT FOR FIVE AND A HALF, AND I'M TELLIN' YOU, THAT'S MY COMMISSION GONE... I'M WORKING FOR NOTHING HERE.

I'M ONLY DOING THIS BECAUSE YOU'RE A LOVELY COUPLE... OF CRIMINALS... AND I CAN SEE HOW HAPPY IT WILL MAKE YOU BOTH.

NOW, IF YOU CAN JUST SIGN HERE, HERE, HERE, HERE, HERE, HERE, AND HERE... AND HERE.

NOW, I'M OBLIGED TO TELL YOU THAT THAT LAST ONE WAS A SPECIAL ONE, TO WAIVE YOUR RIGHT TO A STATUTORY COOLING OFF PERIOD, YOU SEE THAT'S JUST IN CASE YOU CHANGE YOUR MIND, VERY IMPORTANT THAT, ISN'T IT?

SCRIBBLE! SCRIBBLE!

DO YOU REALISE YOU'VE PROBABLY DOUBLED THE VALUE OF YOUR PROPERTY, I LIKE TO THINK THAT'S WHY IT'S CALLED DOUBLE GLAZING. NOW OF COURSE YOUR HEATING BILLS WILL BE HALVED, BUT WHAT ABOUT HEAT LOSS IN OTHER AREAS?

DO YOU KNOW THAT 90% OF ALL HEAT LOSS FROM THE HOME IS LOST DIRECTLY THROUGH THE ROOF?

NINETY PER CENT? THAT'S TERRIBLE ISN'T IT RUPERT?

WHY DON'T YOU JUST FUCK OFF BEFORE I BLOW YOUR BRAINS OUT?

NOW, IT MAY SEEM PERSISTANT BUT IT'S IN YOUR INTEREST, YOU SEE. I'M ACTUALLY TRYING TO SAVE YOU MONEY...

...ON AN ANNUAL GAS BILL OF £400, IT'LL PAY FOR ITSELF IN SIX MONTHS, SO THAT'S NINE THOUSAND POUNDS WELL SPENT.

HOLD ON, WHAT IS IT YOU'RE SELLING NOW?

I'M NOT SELLING ANYTHING. THIS PRODUCT SELLS ITSELF. IT'S A KIND OF HIGH-TECH SPRAY-ON MERINGUE, A MAN IN A DUST MASK AND OVERALLS SIMPLY SPRAYS IT ALL OVER THE UNDERSIDE OF YOUR ROOF, IT LEAVES YOUR ROOF MAINTENANCE-FREE, AND WILL LAST INTO THE NEXT MILLENIUM.

RIGHT. WE BLOW HIS FUCKIN' BRAINS OUT.

HOLD ON RUPERT... SO, IT'S WATERPROOFING AND INSULATION IN JUST ONE APPLICATION?

THAT'S RIGHT, AND WITH OUR EASY-PAY INSTALLMENTS SYSTEM YOU DON'T HAVE TO PAY ANYTHING FOR FOUR YEARS, EXCEPT THE DEPOSIT, AND THE MONTHLY INSTALLMENTS...

... AND THE FINAL BALANCE.

NOW ALL I NEED IS A SIGNATURE ... HERE ... HERE ... HERE ... HERE ... .. AND HERE.

BOOM! BOOM!

HELLO THERE, I WAS IN THE AREA AND I JUST THOUGHT I'D MAKE A COURTESY CALL ... MY THESE GATES ARE IMPRESSIVE AREN'T THEY, MIND I'LL BET THEY LET A LOT OF DRAUGHTS IN, AND THEN THERE'S THE COST OF MAINTENANCE...

HAVE YOU CONSIDERED UPVC REPLACEMENT?

Lady C takes toyboy lover

LADY Clementine Churchill, widow of the former Prime Minister Sir Winston, could be set to re-marry.

Lady Churchill has lead a reclusive life since her husband, who won the war, died in 1965. But rumours of romance have blossomed since January when she was photographed holidaying in Barbados with teenage pop singer Nathan out of Brother Beyond.

Ice-Cream

The couple were seen playing tennis, swimming and sharing a romantic pool side ice cream.

Transit

More recently they have been seen out and about in London, shopping in Oxford Street and dining at the exclusive Beefeater steakhouse at Piccadilly Circus. And a pal of Lady Churchill yesterday admitted that the couple have become 'virtually inseparable'.

Commer

Nathan out of Brother Beyond has enjoyed the company of a string of beautiful women since the arse fell out of his pop career 8 years ago, among them that posh TV presenting 'it' bird with no tits, Tara what's-her-face. But now he seems to have found his perfect match, despite the fact that Lady Churchill is more than five times his age.

Above: The new boy in her life - Nathan out of Brother Beyond.

"In many ways they're perfect for each other", our source revealed. "Since Sir Winston died Clementine has been staying in a lot and watching telly. But Nathan makes her so happy. It's marvellous to see her up and about and smiling again. Their interests are the same. The age gap makes no difference at all".

Luton

Word is that no date has yet been set for a marriage, but rumours of a £2 million engagement ring - paid for out of royalties from Brother Beyond hits such as 'The Harder I Try' - are already circulating in society circles.

'Marriage not beyond possibility' says pal

Lady Churchill pictured with her late husband Sir Winston prior to when he died yesterday.

GOOD NEWS MRS BADER. THERE'S GOING TO BE THE PATTER OF TINNY FEET

OPERATING THEATRE

Cont. over

Volca-NO to Howerd's controversial TV show

A woman who survived the Pompeii disaster yesterday branded comedian Frankie Howerd 'sick' after he announced plans to have made a comedy series about it in the seventies.

Octavia Johnson, 64, was only 3 years old when a massive volcanic eruption swept away her Roman villa and destroyed the ill-fated city where her entire family had lived. And now she's blown her top over plans for a crude television spoof of the infamous tragedy.

Speed

The volcano Vesuvius erupted with such speed that Octavia's father, a mechanic in the Roman army, was turned to stone as he worked underneath a chariot. Octavia only survived because her quick thinking mum managed to grab her and climb up an olive tree as the smegma approached.

Dope

That was many years ago, but Octavia, who now has two children and five grandchildren of her own, is haunted by memories of the disaster to this very day. And yesterday she described plans for a light hearted TV series entitled 'Up Pompeii' as "disgusting".

Whizz

Sources close to the BBC admit that the controversial series, which is due to be filmed in the seventies, will have contained jokes about volcanoes erupting and people being turned into stone.

Frankie Howerd is consoled by large breasted women as a storm brews over his proposed 70s TV show yesterday.

However Mrs Johnson certainly will not be having watched the show. "I know I was only 3 at the time and my memories are very vague, but I couldn't bear the thought of watching the TV and seeing Frankie Howerd make a joke about an actor who might of been portraying my father", she said last night as tears welled in her eyes.

Frankie Howerd, who was still alive when he made the TV series, has since died. But last night he was quick to defend the show against accusations of bad taste. "Ooooh, no missus... don't... stop it", he said, while putting his hands up his back.

A faded old Roman photograph (above) is all that Mrs Octavia Johnson (right) has to remind her of the brave father who she never knew. Yesterday.

Anne Nightingale stang in Berkeley Square

FORMER Radio One DJ Anne Nightingale was being comforted by friends late last night after being stang by a wasp in Berkeley Square.

Miss Nightingale, who presented a request show on Sunday evenings during the 1970s, had travelled from her home in Brighton to Berkeley Square for a cup of tea. Witnesses report hearing her say "Ouch" when the wasp stung her.

Bremner

Police had received several unconfirmed reports of a wasp in Berkeley Square prior to the attack. A Metropolitan Police spokesman said that he suspected Miss Nightingale, 70, may of ate a bun in Berkeley Square and that there might of been all jam on her mouth when the wasp struck.

Bunter

This is the second time that Miss Nightingale has been the victim of yellow and black stripey insects. For two years ago giant bees attacked her and kidnapped her legs during a visit to Peru.

Liar

Although they was never caught, an insect gang known as the 'Busy Bees' were believed to have been responsible. Under the leadership of the late Arthur Askey, bees the size of coconuts comb Peru looking for legs to kidnap and present to their leader at his Aztec temple hideaway. As each gift is received Askey grins through bottle bottom

Anne Nightingale - stunged yesterday in Berkeley Square

glasses and utters the ceremonial words "Ay thang-yow".

The Kid

A Foreign Office spokesman yesterday reassured British tourists that Peru remains a safe holiday destination, but recommended that intending travellers take what he called 'sensible' precautions.

"We would recommend that anyone visiting Peru visit their GP and have their legs inoculated against kidnap by coconut sized bees", he told us.

Modern Times

Both Miss Nightingale and Arthur Askey was last night unavailable for comment.

CLONE YOUR OWN HITLER

Send £6.99 for complete kit. Contains all you need to genetically engineer your own genocidal despot. Get trains, busses etc. running on time -or your money back

PECK Laboratories Ltd. 60 High St. Brazil

ANDY CRAPP   by REG SHYTE

No. 2,563,281

WAR GAMES

TRUE COMMANDO ACTION STORIES OF MEN AT WAR BATTLE PICTURE LIBRARY

FOR those Allied troops taken prisoner during the Second World War, life in the German POW camps was grim indeed. Playing cards was strictly forbidden, and any prisoners caught so doing were sent to the most notorious camp of all -*Stalag Luft 66*

But even here, the spirit of the men was not broken. Captain Frank Tyler was in charge of the games committee at Stalag Luft 66

1800 hours in the prisoners barracks

Then Sergeant 'Rita' Hayworth spoke

The interruption came from Lieutenant 'Taffy' Macay, who had just arrived at Stalag Luft 66

The young Lieutenant outlined his plan to dig a large hole underneath the barrack room floor, in which the giant game of Twister could be played, out of sight of the German guards.

And so work began on digging a large hole under the barracks...

...and sewing blankets together to make a big Twister mat.

One week later, everything was prepared

Above ground, Ginger played his trumpet to drown out the noise made by his companions below.

All through the night the game continued

And next day, on parade

During the period 1940 - 43, of the 2,396 Allied prisoners taken through the gates of Stalag Luft 66, over 987 managed to play Twister. This story is dedicated to their memory.

53

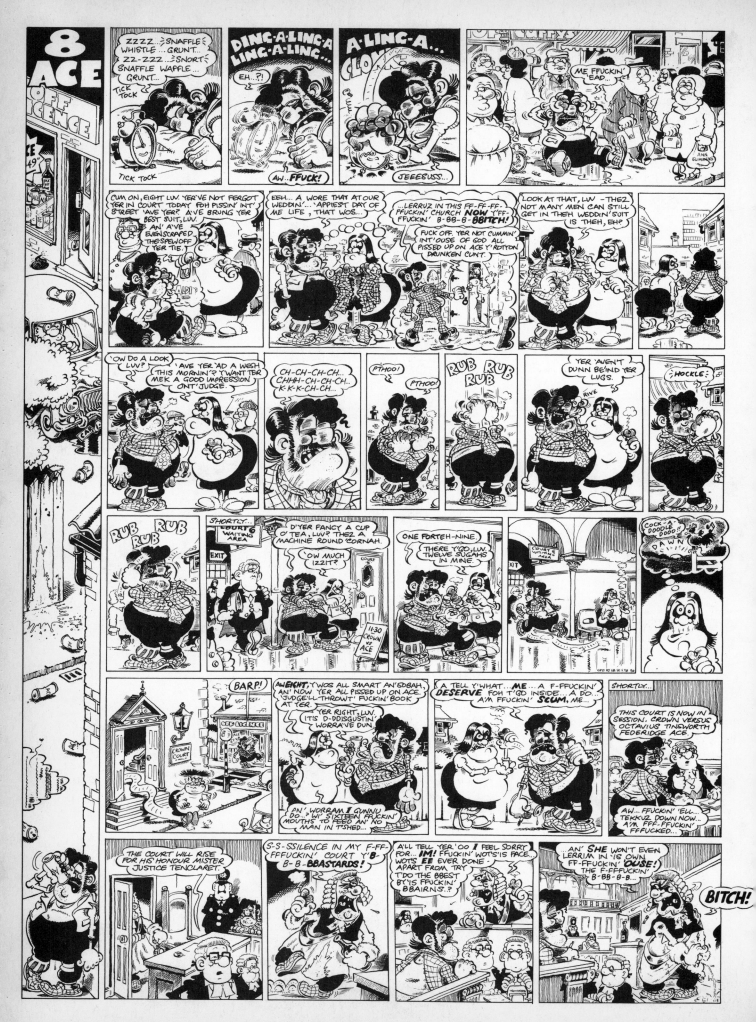

SPACE - THE FINAL INSULT

By our National Disgrace Correspondent

THE heartbroken widow of pointy-eared Star Trek alien Mr Spock yesterday pleaded with Lottery chiefs: "Please don't let me sell my husband's medals to the Klingons".

Edna Spock, 68, from Peterlee in County Durham, has been living on social security hand-outs since her space husband Mr Spock died in the second Star Trek film. And now, facing growing weekly bills for bingo and cigarettes, she has reluctantly decided to sell her late husbands treasured collection of military medals.

Hope

"I promised Mr Spock that I would never part with the medals as long as I lived", said Mrs Spock yesterday. "But now that I am going to sell them, I only hope that the Lottery pay a small fortune for them and that they can stay in the country".

Monkhouse

Mr Spock, the emotionless Vulcan science officer who sprang to fame during the first Star Trek television series, won of hatful of Federation medals for battling the Klingons during a 28 year TV space career. But ironically it is wealthy Klingon collectors who are most likely to snap up the medals when they come under the hammer at an auction of Intergalactic Memorabilia to be held at Christies in London later this month.

Dylan

Spock's gongs include the Federation Bravery Medal that he received one week for climbing up a pipe to reverse the polarity of the dilithium crystals, and a special Federation Commendation Cap he was awarded by Captain Kirk for remaining at his post while the bridge of the ship shook about during alien attacks.

Zebedee

Eager collectors of space militaria could pay anything up to £50,000 for the unique collection. Only last year a medal awarded to Avon out of Blake's 7 was sold at auction for

Mrs Spock (above) treasures the space medal earned by her brave husband Mr Spock (below).

£5,500 to an anonymous giant spider bidding by phone from the planet Metabilis 3.

Florence

Experts fear that Spock's medals will also leave the planet, boldly going where no Star Trek medal has gone before - into the hands of pastie-headed, goaty-bearded, war-like Klingon collectors.

Milan

But Viz is launching a campaign to keep Spock's medals in Blighty. We believe they are a vital part of our National Heritage, and we want Lottery chiefs to cough up the cash to buy them back for Britain.

Spock's heirloom collection of space medals (above) selectively coated in 22 carat gold and accompanied by a wood and glass display case and Certificate of Authenticity.

"It's dis-guss-ting all that money being spent on a Dome for gays and child molesters when only a few millions of pounds would keep these priceless space medals in Britain", said a daft, bigoted cow yesterday.

Viz says SAVE Spock's Medals

Captain Kirk, now a corset wearing wiggy fruitcake, believes it would be wrong for Spock's medals to fall into enemy hands, despite the fact that the Klingons now maintain an uneasy peace with the Federation. Speaking from his death bed on the Channel Island of Alderney where he now lives in a giant cuckoo clock, he pleaded for Lottery chiefs to intervene.

Rome

"He may have been totally emotionless, but Spock would be raising an eye-

brow quizzically in his grave if he knew what was going on", he told us. "I'm sure he would find it all very highly illogical". Captain Kirk, who has been dying of space piles since 1988, bravely agreed to start the ball rolling by donating £1.50 to our campaign.

Spock's medals could be sold to KLINGONS

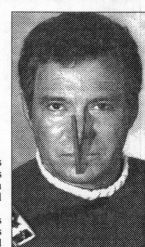

Fruitcake Kirk thinks this whole thing stinks.

LATEST NEWS

TITANIC SINKS

THE Titanic, the world's biggest newspaper story, has sunk in what may prove to be the greatest tabloid disaster in living memory. And there are grave fears for over 2,000 journalists who were on board.

The story, launched in 1912, was a 'floating palace' for tabloid journalists who have used it to fill endless column inches for many months. Indeed, newspaper editors thought it was unsinkable.

But despite warnings of growing disinterest, the story steamed at high speed into a wall of public indifference. Reports indicate she is listing heavily and going arse-up in the water. Unless another story appears quickly to pick up the survivors, many jobs could be lost.

Turin

Several Sun journalists have been spotted clinging

TITANIC LOST
Grave loss of life is feared

The story pictured in 1912.

desperately to items of debris, including readers childish drawings of Leonardo Di Caprio and Kate Winslett. Among passengers known to be on board is Mr Piers Morgan, editor of the Daily Mirror, who was last seen wearing women's clothing in the vicinity of the lifeboats.

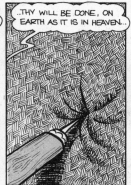

FEARS GROW OVER RAC ORANGE MARCH

A planned RAC orange march is to go ahead in Birmingham next month, despite protests from AA members.

The RAC, who recently changed their corporate colour scheme to orange from the traditional red, white and blue, plan to march through the predominantly AA district of Bournville to celebrate the anniversary of their first ever roadside recovery.

Zephyr

In the historic road rescue an RAC officer riding a primitive motorcycle beat an AA mechanic to a broken down Ford Zephyr on the A38 near Edgbaston, and famously managed to jump start the vehicle. The event is commemorated annually, but this year's chosen route - along the hard shoulder of the M5 past the headquarters of the AA - has been labelled 'provocative' and has rekindled deep felt feelings of bitterness and resentment which exist between the rival motoring communities.

Sirocco

Last night there were calls for calm from Birmingham police chiefs amidst fears that the AA is planning its own retaliatory march along the predominantly RAC Smethwick Road. P.C. McGarrett, Community Liaison Officer at Smethwick police station, issued a plea for reason to members of both organisations. "Already fragile relations are set to break down unless common sense is allowed to prevail", he said yesterday.

Mistral

Meanwhile the Rev. Ian Polkadot, leader of the hard-line Green Flag organisation, accused the AA of being sodomites, and having an average response time of well over an hour.

"The AA are the homosexual whores of hell and the sons of Satan! May God strike them down in the filthy cesspits where they lie. We the Green Flag have been chosen by Jesus to repair vehicles at the roadside. And if we don't get to your car within 1 hour we'll give you £10", balled the Rev. Polkadot yesterday.

An AA yellow march passes angry broken down Green Flag members in the staunchly RAC district of Solihull yesterday.

Firemen have had their chips

THE chips are down for Britain's fire fighters, according to union bosses. For microwave cookers and the growth of convenience foods could soon consign our famous red fire engines to the dust bin.

According to fire chiefs the rise in popularity of MicroChips - the convenient if unpleasant tasting alternative to real chipped potatoes - may have sounded the death knell for Britain's brave fire fighting forces. For MicroChips, which cook in seconds inside a micro-wave oven, alleviate the need for drunken pub goers to attempt deep fat frying late at night.

Passat

Since 1980 the number of chip pan fires attended after pub closing time has halved, according to official figures. And increasingly fire crews are having to rely on electrical faults and arson at school premises to scrape a living.

Twister

"Unless we act now the traditional British chip pan fire will soon be a thing of the past". That's the view of Barney McGrew, general secretary of the fire fighters

Angry fire fighters ponder their future as bosses announced a further cut in house fires yesterday

union the F.F.U. He believes the government should act now to encourage more drunken people to undertake dangerous deep fat frying.

Buckaroo

But the Prime Minister's father-in-law, 'scouse git' human chip pan actor Tony Booth, yesterday ruled out any such move. "It is inconceivable that a Labour government would en-

courage people coming home from the pub to turn chip pans on and then fall asleep", he boasted to drunken soldiers in a Hampstead pub last night.

Sandwich

Meanwhile under-pressure Home Secretary Jack Straw refused to confirm that the government were considering a plan to promote more smoking in bed.

DARTS player John Lowe broke down in tears yesterday as he told a Nottingham court how Larry Grayson's teeth bit him as they tried to escape from his mouth.

Lowe, 52, of The Park, Nottingham, is claiming damages and compensation against Mrs Ethel Grayson, widow of the former TV light entertainer, who he claims sold him the teeth which were unfit for the purpose for which they were intended.

Mousetrap

The court heard how Mr Lowe, a fan of Larry Grayson, attended a sale of the star's personal effects shortly after his death in 1993. He purchased several items including a chair and the teeth for which he paid £625.

He wore them without incident for several weeks until one day in March 1994 when, after attending a darts exhibition match in Skegness, he went outside and attempted to whistle for a taxi.

Fondue

Suddenly he became aware of the teeth attempting to get out of his mouth. Instinctively he tried to wrestle the teeth back in, and in the struggle that ensued he was severely bitten on the chin, the

The offending teeth pictured in Mr Lowe's mouth (above) and seen during happier times with their original owner Larry Grayson (below)

resulting wound requiring hospital treatment. The teeth escaped, but were later recovered from a bench at Skegness railway station.

Pastie

Speaking in Mrs Grayson's defence Sir Christmas Fartface QC told the court that the teeth had been sold "as seen", and his client had always assumed they were to be kept as a souvenir, for display purposes only. She had not been aware that Mr Lowe intended to use them for eating or smiling.

Foreskin

Mr Lowe is claiming £2,000 damages plus unlimited compensation for distress caused by the incident. The case was adjourned until Monday.

SPOT the CLUE 1999

WITH CELEBRITY BOTANIST DAVID BELLAMY

GWEETINGS, SPACE-MYSTEWY FANS. I'VE GOT A TWEMENDOUS YARN FOR YOU THIS WEEK — IT'S CALLED THE CASE OF THE FEATHERY COUNTESS (IN SPACE)

THE STORY BEGINS IN THE FUTURE, ON THE MOON, ANCESTRAL HOME OF LORD AND LADY FORSYTH

DO HAVE ANOTHER SPACE-CUCUMBER SANDWICH, REVEREND HITLER

ZANK YOU, LADY FORSYTH

UND VOT A DELIGHTFUL SPACESHIP YOU UND LORD FORSYTH ARE LIVINK IN

YES. THE MOON HAS BEEN IN THE FORSYTH FAMILY FOR GENERATIONS, REVEREND HITLER

YOU MUST TAKE A STROLL AROUND THE ESTATE AFTER TIFFIN

SUDDENLY THE ROOM WAS PLUNGED INTO DARKNESS AND A PIERCING SCREAM RENT THE AIR

SHRIEK!

AND WHEN THE LIGHTS CAME BACK ON

EGAD! IT'S MY LADY WIFE...

SOMEONE — OR SOMETHING — HAS QUITE LITERALLY STUFFED HER ARSE FULL OF FEATHERS

HELLO? POLICE? THIS IS LORD FORSYTH, ON THE MOON

I'D LIKE TO REPORT MY WIFE'S ARSE BEING STUFFED FULL OF FEATHERS

MOMENTS LATER THE SPACE POLICE WERE ON THE SCENE

AFTERNOON, CONSTABLE — I'M INSPECTOR SHARPE OF SCOTLAND YARD

NOW — WHICH ONE IS LADY FORSYTH?

BANG! BANG!

BANG! BANG!

I'M FRIGHTFULLY SORRY ABOUT THAT, INSPECTOR — THE SIGHT OF MY WIFE'S BIG FEATHERY ARSE STICKING UP IN THE AIR WAS JUST TOO TEMPTING

SHE LOOKED LIKE A GIANT PHEASANT OR GROUSE, AND I SIMPLY COULDN'T RESIST BLASTING AWAY WITH MY SHOTGUN

DON'T BLAME YOURSELF, LORD FORSYTH — IT WASN'T YOUR FAULT

FOR WHOEVER STUFFED HER LADYSHIP'S ARSE WITH FEATHERS KNEW THAT YOUR NATURAL ARISTOCRATIC HUNTING INSTINCTS WOULD COMPEL YOU TO SHOOT HER

BUT INSPECTOR, WHAT KIND OF EVIL PERSON WOULD WANT MY WIFE TO BE KILLED?

THAT'S WHAT I INTEND TO FIND OUT, LORD FORSYTH

OUTSIDE, A THOROUGH SEARCH WAS MADE OF THE MOON

INSPECTOR SHARPE — OVER HERE!

WHAT IS IT, CONSTABLE DODGSON?

IN THE SHRUBBERY, SIR — A FEATHER!

HM. AND IT'S LYING BESIDE THAT NEWLY CUT FLOWER

YES SIR. A SPECIMEN OF ROSA CANINA — COMMONLY KNOWN AS THE DOG-ROSE

THE VERY SAME SPECIES WHICH REVEREND HITLER IS WEARING IN HIS LAPEL

I'VE A SHREWD IDEA WHO THE CULPRIT IS, CONSTABLE DODGSON

I'D LIKE EVERYONE GATHERED IN THE SPACE-SHIP DRAWING ROOM IN TEN MINUTES TIME

GENTLEMEN, THE IDENTITY OF THE BADDIE IS......

IT WAS YOU WHO FILLED LADY FORSYTH'S BUM WITH FEATHERS THUS CAUSING HER DEATH. REVEREND HITLER WAS MERELY A RED HERRING

...CONSTABLE DODGSON!

BUT HER LADYSHIP HAD THREATENED TO CUT ME OUT OF HER WILL — AND SO I HAD TO MURDER HER

YES, DAMN YOU, I DID IT. I AM LADY FORSYTH'S ILLEGITIMATE BROTHER, AND HEIR TO THE MOON

I ONLY WANTED TO INHERIT THE MOON

I ONLY WANTED TO INHERIT THE MOON, INSPECTOR

AND YOU WOULD HAVE SUCCEEDED, CONSTABLE BUT YOU MADE ONE SILLY MISTAKE...

DAVID BELLAMY SAYS: DID YOU SPOT THE CLUE?

WHEN CONSTABLE DODGSON REFERRED TO THE DOG-ROSE BY ITS LATIN NAME, HE CALLED IT 'ROSA CANINA' — USING CAPITAL LETTERS...

BUT AS EVERY BOTANIST KNOWS, THE LATIN NAMES FOR PLANTS ARE ALWAYS SPELT IN LOWER CASE LETTERS. THUS, CONSTABLE DODGSON SHOULD HAVE SAID 'ROSA canina'

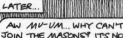

Letterbocks

and horse's cocks. Sorry. There was a gap.

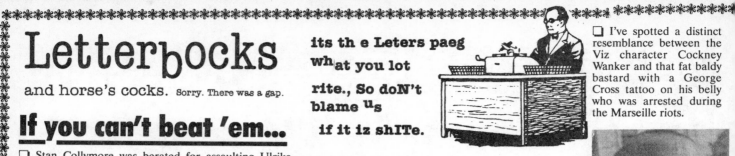

its th e Leters paeg wh at you lot rite., So doN't blame us if it iz shITe.

If you can't beat 'em...

❑ Stan Collymore was berated for assaulting Ulrika Jonsson. And Paul Gasgoine took a lot of stick for alleged wife-beating. But at least these two England rejects got the aggression out of their system.
Perhaps if David Beckham had layed into Posh Spice a few times before going to France he wouldn't have felt the need to kick that Argentinian.

**James Hill
Camberley**

Letterbocks
PO Box 1PT
Newcastle upon Tyne
NE99 1PT

Fax: 0191 2414244
viz.comic@virgin.net

Revelation

❑ The Popemobile has 3 inch thick bullet-proof glass in its windows. There's fucking faith for you.

**Doc Choc
Windsor**

❑ Why aren't all cars made out of Lego? That way after a crash we could simply put our cars back together again ourselves, instead of paying the high prices which garages charge for repairs.
There'd be other advantages too. If you were caught in a traffic jam for instance, you could simply turn your car into a helicopter, although would probably need more bricks.
It's got to be worth thinking about. Unless of course the car manufacturers and garages don't want us saving money, and are only interested in protecting their profits.

**Chris Mappley
Carshalton**

❑ Our son was so sad to see the departure of his favourite Spice Girl Geri. But after sulking for a few days he cheered himself up by writing a little ode in her honour. He's not normally a poet, but even my wife agrees this isn't a bad effort.
*Ginger Spice is twice as nice,
As that fucker Scary,
Cos her tits are twice as big,
And her cunt more hairy.*
Do any other readers have Spice Girl poems they'd care to share?

**Peter Wright
Grimsby**

Mice to Big 'C' you, to Big 'C' you, mice

❑ So, scientists claim to have found a cure for cancer in mice. Big deal. That's great news if you happen to be a mouse. Why don't these idiots try finding a cancer cure for people? After all, its us who pay their wages through our taxes. Not mice.

**Mrs G. Day
Cullercoats**

Post mortem

❑ "The female of the species is more deadly than the mail", sang that bloke out of Space. Try telling that to my uncle. He was killed by a letter bomb.

**Paul Smith
Nottingham**

Fuckface

❑ I couldn't help noticing a distinct resemblance between Sun columnist Gary Bushell and the Honey Pot 'vibrating vagina' as advertised in the classified pages of down market skud magazines. I wonder if perhaps they are both twats?

**S. Suds
Dishforth**

❑ You often see signs outside churches telling us that "Jesus Lives". But these religious folk are always carping on about how he died on the cross for all our sins. Dying isn't much of a sacrifice if you're planning on coming back again five minutes later.
Come on God botherers. You can't have it both ways. Make up your minds. Is he dead or is he alive?

**Mr S. Turd
Corbridge**

❑ I read somewhere that Jodie Foster wants to be artificially inseminated with the sperm of the perfect man. Well darling, I'm 5'4", weigh 15 stone, have a William Hague hairstyle and a good job as a shoe salesman in Freeman Hardy Willis in Macclesfield. Just give me the word and I'll be on my way, complete with a turkey baster and pickle jar, to make your dreams come true.

**Derek Nobbs
Macclesfield**

❑ I've spotted a distinct resemblance between the Viz character Cockney Wanker and that fat baldy bastard with a George Cross tattoo on his belly who was arrested during the Marseille riots.

I wonder if perhaps they are both wankers.

**D.B.
Saaf Landan**

❑ Women say that men are only after one thing. Rubbish! I'm after two, tops AND fingers.

**Lee Nelson
Stockton-on-Tees**

❑ Thank heavens for coconuts. How else could we make the delightful "clip clop" sound of horses cantering?

**Shaz
London NW1**

Give the old dog a bone

❑ I recently had an affair with a mature woman, 25 years older than myself. I can recommend the experience to any other readers who, like myself, are too overweight and ugly to get off with a decent looking bird their own age.

**Mark Palmer
Leeds**

❑ They've had that much mileage out of her, you'd think that the BBC could afford to buy Maureen from Driving School a fucking set of teeth. For Christ's sake, she frightens my dog.

**T. Kettle
London**

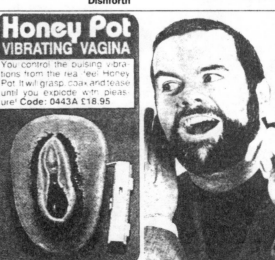

Honey Pot VIBRATING VAGINA
You control the pulsing vibrations from the real feel Honey Pot. It will grasp, coax and tease until you explode with pleasure! Code: 0443A £18.95

64

TOP TIPS

JANET Street-Porter's boyfriend. invite Janet for a game of 'wheelbarrow' in the garden this autumn. Hey presto! You'll have raked up all the leaves in minutes.

Nathan-Madonna Byers
Oxford (if you don't mind)

FOOL passers-by into thinking you're a stranded time traveller by asking them what the date is, and then gasping and shaking your head in disbelief when they tell you.

Wayne Kerr (geddit?)
Birmingham

BORED housewives? Recreate the excitement of a Tom and Jerry cartoon by standing on a stool wearing red socks and shouting "Thomas! Thomas!"

C.M.
Surrey

OLD folk. Don't buy expensive coffins. Invest in a luxury single pine wardrobe instead. That way you'll also get some use out of it while you're still alive.

McM
London SE4

FOOL passers by into thinking you keep a bird of prey by walking down the street wearing a leather gauntlet, waving a piece of raw meat in your hand and constantly looking up at the sky.

Simone Glover
Tottenham

ANNOY saggy bladdered old men by standing next to them in the toilet and peeing as hard and as fast as you can, while making satisfied "Aaaah!" noises. Then one quick shake and away.

Ben
Camden

Michael WEATHERMAN OF HEARTS

A heartfelt tribute to the beloved *Michael, Weatherman of Hearts*, brought to life on a Signature Edition Commemorative Porcelain Peter Piper Picked a Peck of Pickled Pepper Portrait Plate.

Michael Fish, BBC weatherman. With a glakey grin and a casual gesticulation of the left arm he forecast the weather, and gave false hope to those of us planning barbecues. He selflessly warned us about overnight frosts, low pressure fronts and high pollen counts.

But now he is gone - on holiday for two weeks. With a wink and a smile he has bid us goodbye. But his meteorological knowledge, his nondescript broadcasting style and the tireless effort he devoted to co-ordinating training courses for African weathermen are the legacy he leaves behind.

Now you can honour his memory with *Michael, Weatherman of Hearts*, a magnificent collector plate from acclaimed meteorological portrait artist, Sveti Arse.

In the tradition of the most prized collectibles, this heirloom collector plate is crap. Crafted of the finest quality fibrous cellulose, each plate is painstakingly printed and hand bordered in Platignum permanent marker pen. Priced not thirty, not twenty, not ten, not even five pounds.

Who'll give me twenty quid for a dozen of these lovely plates. Come along now, just £20 for 12.

There, you, lady at the back...

Tic-Tat Mint - The Fuckwit's Choice in Collectible Tat

TO SUPPORT THE CHARITIES CLOSE TO MICHAEL FISH'S HEART, FOR EVERY MILLION PLATES SOLD WE PLEDGE TO GIVE SOME OLD PANTS AND AN INCOMPLETE JIGSAW PUZZLE TO THE OXFAM SHOP ROUND THE CORNER.

Michael, Weatherman of Hearts Reservation Order Form

Please post now, before the lady in front of you gets the last ones. They're going like hot cakes.

To: Tic-Tat Mint, Nevernever Lane, London E12.

Yes, me, over here! I'll have two dozen *Michael, Weatherman of Hearts* plates... no, hang on, make it three dozen. Please snatch this £60, which I am waving frantically, out of the envelope before I change my mind.

I enclose sixty pounds cash.

Signature _____ Date _____

Satisfaction guarantee. If we are not completely satisfied with our money we will return it, within 30 days, and you will replace with a larger amount.

When you're HUNGRY but you DON'T want FOOD... NOT FOODLES

Simply add boiling water, leave for 3 minutes, then poke disinterestedly with a fork.

A tasteless alternative to food in FIVE uninteresting flavours...

Nothing Flavour * Bland'n'Spicy Flavour
Chemical Falvour * Boiling Water Flavour
NEW Rubber'n'Sand Flavour

On sale at petrol stations, newsagents, and larger branches of Halfords.

RANDALL & DIANA deceased

Royal Protection Squad officer DS Jack Randall had been one of Diana, Princess of Wales' favourite detectives. Ever since her wedding day Jack had been a loyal and faithful servant.

Throughout her troubled marriage Jack was always there to guard her, protect her, and help her carry any awkwardly shaped bunches of flowers that were given to her by the public.

But after Diana's tragic death Jack decided to leave the force and set up a detective agency of his own. Jack Randall Private Investigations.

But life as a private detective was not as glamourous as protecting the Royals. There were no more trips to exotic places. Instead Jack spent most of his time waiting for the phone to ring.

The phone hasn't rung all week. I'm wasting my time sitting here.

I may as well jack it in and go and work as a security guard at Woolworths.

Don't be silly, Jack. You're a good detective!

Uh? What the...

What's up? You look like you've seen a ghost!

Diana... it can't be. I thought you were dead.

I am, you idiot. Can't you tell? Why else would I be wearing an outfit like this?

Don't worry Jack. I've come back to *help* you, not *haunt* you.

Help me? How?

Come on Jack, with your brain and my spirit, Randall & Diana deceased could be a partnership made in heaven.

Surely you can't be serious...

I am serious Jack. I want to be the Ghost Private Detective of People's Hearts.

Cont. page 71

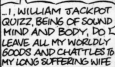

The secret of everlasting life can be <u>YOURS</u>- *for £8.95*

The BRACELET OF IMMORTALITY

Everlasting life for £8.95! **I don't believe it.**
Well it's **TRUE!**
The House of Methuselah is pleased to offer you 'The Bracelet of Immortality' at a never to be repeated price of £8.95. Hand beaten from the purest Eternium, a metal famed for its life-giving properties, The Bracelet of Immortality is available in men's and women's sizes, and is both attractive and durable.

NO RISK TRIAL PERIOD

We are so convinced of the eternal life-giving effects of the Bracelet of Immortality, that we will give you a full refund if, within 30 days, you have not lived forever. Simply return the bracelet. You have nothing to lose.

AUTHENTIC TESTIMONIALS

I was sceptical until my wife bought a Bracelet of Immortality. But it *really does work*. Now I've got one too and we're both going to live for ever. We're thinking of getting them for the kids. T.C. Doncaster

I bought my Bracelet of Immortality seven years ago and have enjoyed the benefits of life eternal ever since. R.T. Chesterfield

I tried everything to become immortal and nothing worked. Then a friend recommended your Bracelet of Immortality. I put it on and immediately began to live for ever. Thank you House of Methuselah. Y.L. Bolton.

I wear my Bracelet of Immortality all the time. I took it off once to clean the car and nearly died. I haven't taken it off since. G.L. Swindon.

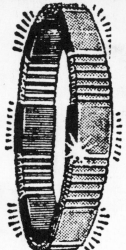

Order Now
Send to: Lifelong Industries, Gullible House, Ely

I don't want to die. Please send me .... Bracelets of Immortality. I enclose £.....
Name..........Address..........
Callers are not welcome at our offices and will be refused entry

Eternal life, for £8.95 also makes a great gift for a friend or loved one

---

BOWLS TALK!

BORED OLD MEN JUST WAITING TO TALK ABOUT BOWLS WITH YOU!!

I g✱t one q✱ite close to the jack recently
0774 12312

My cap is v✱ry, v✱ry flat. V✱ry, v✱ry flat ind✱✱d.
0774 12313

Ooh! I don't think th✱t one's going to run
0774 12314

Bowlingly Explicit!! No long intros, you're straight into the bowls talk!!!

Calls cost 45 pence (9/- in old money) per minute and terminate in Frinton-on-Sea

---

BOWELS TALK!!
Biddy-Line International

Enid, 75, is having terrible trouble down there, round the back ● 0774 123 11

Ada hasn't been for 3 weeks... and she'll tell you about it ● 0774 123 12

Minnie keeps needing to go, but when she gets there, she can't ● 0774 123 11

Dolly is regular as clockwork. 7.30 every morning. Without fail. ● 0774 123 16

Eggs just don't agree with Mabel, and she'd love to tell you why ● 0774 123 13

Mavis, 84, will tell you about her sister's diarrhoea in 30 seconds ● 0774 123 14

Eavesdrop on Cissy and Eunice talking frankly about their piles
● 0774 123 15

All calls cost far too much these days, you know and terminate in a queue in the Post Office. Warning: Biddy-Line International calls will go on and on and on

---

EX-TOASTER ENGINEER REVEALS UNKNOWN SECRETS!!

The book Tefal tried to BAN!

Would 100 slices of toast a day, EVERY day, make a difference to you? In this highly acclaimed book an ex-toaster engineer reveals all the latest pop-up tricks you need to make any toaster cough up toast again and again! Most of what you will read is not published in the toaster manuals!

*Which machines to use and when ***The secrets** of the Browning button. ***Toasting** cycles- once you're making toast, how to **keep** making it
This book describes the method used by engineers to test the toasters, and by using it you can empty any toaster in minutes. It's amazingly simple and works on nearly every toaster made within the last three years.

"We made 180 slices of toast in one hour using this guide" -GQ Magazine

Name........................
Address....................
....
.................Post Code......
Please allow forever for delivery.

Yes! Please rush me my copy of "The Insider Guide to Toasters" I enclose payment of £15.99 understand precious little.
Call our 24 hour credit card hotline. Dial 100 and ask for 'Freephone Toast'
Send postal order or cash, but preferably cash to- Brass Neck Publishing, Box 34. Hull

---

NOBODY! - REPEAT - <u>NOT NOBODY!</u> - BEATS OUR PRICES!!!!

THIS MUST BE BRITAIN'S LOWEST PRICE Men's Trousers

ONLY £1.99 A PAIR inc. P&P
UP TO 7' 4" WAIS

NEVER in our wildest dreams could we imagine offering trousers at £1.99 a pair, not even if we'd been eating cheese at bedtime. So <u>HOW</u> is it <u>POSSIBLE?</u>

One of our biggest suppliers has been stitched up by a circus cancelling a massive order for trousers for side show freaks. We've stepped in and bulk purchased the entire order at a fraction of the normal price and now our warehouse is FULL TO EXPLODING! We've got to get rid of them IMMEDIATELY before we're all BLOWN TO SMITHEREENS!

WE'VE SMASHED THE PRICE, YOU GRAB THE BARGAINS!

These trousers have many of the features you'd expect from the most expensive, proper trousers, for example- two legs, some pockets, a zip etc, and expertly tailored with a generous waistline and parsimonious inside leg. They're beautifully made from 100% 4,4,2, poly-L-cyanoacrylate Crumplene, renowned for its combination of hard wearing good looks and pyro accelerant properties.

✱ Deep, pension book-sized pockets ✱ Chunky rust-proof zip ✱ Dew drop drip dry, stain resistant gusset ✱ 2 - YES 2! - sturdy belt loops

We occasionally make our misfits parade of a mailing list available to others who sell clothes to people too ashamed to go into shops. ❑ Tick this box if you like

Waist	Inside leg	4"	7"
No. of pairs of trousers that you want			
6' 6"			
7' 4"			
	Total		

Name............................
Address.........................
I enclose £........ for my trousers
Send to: **Cheap-E-Kegs Ltd.
The Exploding Trouser Warehouse,
Knowsley, West Yorkshire**

FOOLHARDY HOLIDAYS

For a change this year, why not come
Motorcycling through Glass?

Here at GlassBreaks, we have 25 years experience looking after the holidaymaker who wants to motorcycle through glass.

Use of motorcycle and all sheets of glass are included in the price, whether you motorcycle through 2 sheets of glass a day... or 200! There are NO hidden extras! And the kids can join in too with our monkey bikes.
Whatever the weather, you're guaranteed a smashing time at GlassBreaks

I would like to motorcycle through some glass this year. Please send me details. Name..........Address..........
GlassBreaks. Brecon Airfield, Brecon, Wales

FRUSTRATING HOLIDAYS

String Breaks

Spend an aggravating week or fortnight untangling kites in Devon and Cornwall. Hotels in beautiful surroundings in the heart of the West Country. Bed, breakfast, evening meal and tangled kites from £350 per week, per person. Send for details

A happy camper gets to grips with his kite...

String Breaks, Tangly farm, Bodmin, Cornwall

IRKSOME CRUISES

NORFOLK BROADS
SEPT
£99 PER BOAT SLP 4

Spend a week to ten days on board our luxury 6 berth cabin cruisers, trying to find your keys. Meander through some of Britain's most tranquil and unspoilt countryside, as our rep asks for the hundredth time where you last saw them.

TEL: **01692 5822**

Depressed? Suicidal? Nobody to turn to?

At times, we all find it difficult to cope. If you're feeling like that now, chances are, all you need is someone to talk to. But please , don't call us... we'd rather not get involved

The Pharisees
Telephone: somebody else

The Pharisees. Walking by on the other side- *24 hrs a day*

Cont. from page 66

Later that day Jack had a visitor.

Jack Randall?

Yeah, that's me.

Hello. My name is Mr Edwards.

Most of Jack's work was routine stuff involving adultery and divorce. It looked like this case was going to be no different.

What can I do for you Mr Edwards?

I need your help. You see, it's my wife, Sarah. I think she's having an affair.

Who could blame her, eh Jack? Have you ever seen such an ugly bloke?

Leave it out Di!

Who are you talking to? Did you say Di?

No... I said WHY... WHY do you think your wife is having an affair?

Well, she keeps disappearing on expensive trips abroad.

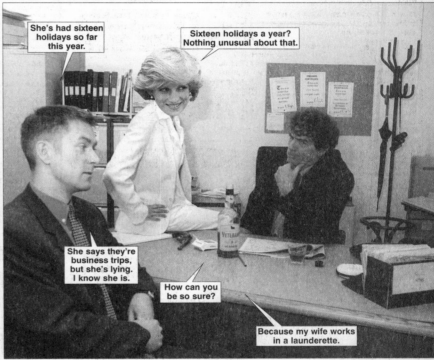

She's had sixteen holidays so far this year.

Sixteen holidays a year? Nothing unusual about that.

She says they're business trips, but she's lying. I know she is.

How can you be so sure?

Because my wife works in a launderette.

Jack decided to take the case, and that night he staked out the Edward's house. It was a quiet night, and by dawn Jack had nodded off.

Zzzzz!

Then suddenly a leggy blonde emerged from the house, her bags packed. It was Sarah Edwards. But Jack was still sound asleep...

Jack! Wake up, you oaf! The bird has flown! You're supposed to follow her.

Sarah Edwards walked to a nearby car and put her bag in the boot. Diana could do nothing to wake Jack up. Mrs Edwards was getting away.

Cont. page 74

Cont. from page 71

Right Jack, give me the keys... Oh no! I can't drive can I?

Wait a minute... I'm a ghost aren't I? I don't need a car. I can go anywhere I want...

Quick as a flash Diana spirited herself away, and reappeared in the passenger seat of Mrs Edwards car as it sped away through the empty city streets.

Hey! Slow down a bit will you!

Where are we going in such a hurry?

What's the matter? Can't you hear me?

Oh no.. you can't, can you. Oh well, never mind.

After a while Mrs Edwards' car pulled up outside a factory gate.

Hey! What are we stopping here for? Is this where you meet your fancy man?

It's not exactly an ideal love nest is it?

Some time later, Di reappeared back in Jack's office.

Where the hell have you been?

Uh?!? Stop appearing like that will you, you scared the life out of me.

Luckily I was able to stay awake this morning, and I followed Mrs Edwards.

Her husband is wrong. She didn't meet another man...

Wait a minute... if there's no-one else's kippers in her grill, why did I spend last night camped outside her house getting a sore neck?

She drove to a factory on the outskirts of town...

"A land mine factory to be precise, where she picked up a land mine and put it in the boot of her car."

LAND MINE FACTORY

"Then she headed straight to the airport and caught the first flight to Africa."

Wait a minute... land mines... airport? Surely you don't mean....

Yes Jack. Her foreign trips are part of a lucrative business... smuggling land mines to Africa!

And dead or alive, I'm determined to put a stop to it.

CONTINUED ON PAGE 129

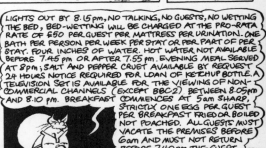

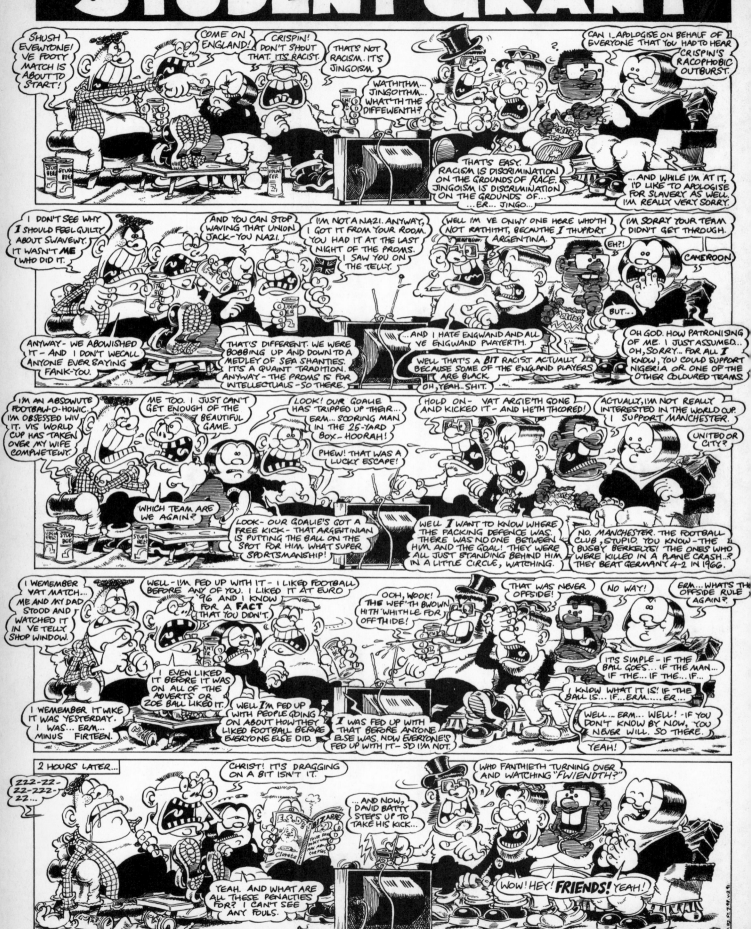

QUEEN MUM AXED!

By our TV Soap Reality/Fiction Blurring Correspondents
Dan Shite & Una Pissflaps

"It's news to me" - actress Liz left in the dark

Actress Liz Bowes-Lyons leaving Stringfellows nightclub with Brian Harvey out of East 17 in happier times. Their marriage lasted two-and- a-half hours.

BRITAIN'S favourite soap star the Queen Mum is set to be axed.

In a move that is sure to shock the entire nation the Queen Mother is to be written out of Britain's longest running soap The Royal Family.

The show's producers made the controversial decision to axe their most popular star at a heated production meeting in London last week. It is the latest in a line of outlandish storylines aimed a boosting the show's flagging ratings.

Shocked

In recent years viewers have been shocked by scenes which have included:

* **ADULTERY** by both the Prince and Princess of Wales.
* **DIVORCE** for both Andrew and Charles.
* **DRAMA** as Windsor Castle burnt down.
* **A STROKE** for heavy smoker Princess Margaret.

At one point there was even talk of a first ever gay Royal romance involving Prince Edward, but this was considered too controversial by the show's senior executives.

Pfeiffer

Critics had claimed that recent raunchy plots were a TURN OFF for the show's traditional audience who have been abandoning the soap in their droves. But following Princess Diana's dramatic exit from the soap in August last year - which made front page news and saw TV audiences quadruple - the show's writers have been under pressure to produce even more controversial storylines.

Ma belle

Elizabeth Bowes-Lyon who plays the Queen Mother was not at the Royal Family's London studios yesterday. However the news came as a shock to the rest of the cast.

The Queen Mum as she is seen by millions of viewers.

"We're a close-knit team", said Elizabeth Windsor who plays the Queen. "We work together and socialise together too. In many ways we're like a real family. This will effect us all. It's a big blow, and it makes you realise that none of us are indispensable".

Sont

Greek actor Phillipos Battenburg, who plays the soap's romeo rat Prince Philip, said the Family would not be the same without the Queen Mum. "She's almost as big as the show itself. When I joined in 1947 I had only just got off a boat from Greece, but Liz sat me down, helped me with my lines and made me feel at home. She's always been an absolute darling and a real professional".

Les

Details of the Queen Mum's exit are being kept a closely guarded secret. Three separate endings will be filmed for her final episode, but not even the cast or film crew will know which one is to be screened.

Mots

Last night no-one from the show's production team was available for comment.

DURHAM born actress Lizzy Bowes-Lyon was last night reeling after we broke the news of her sacking from the long running soap.

Qui

Speaking outside the luxury 6 bedroom Essex ranch which she shares with her boyfriend, Gladiator Wolf, she told us she'd be seeking an urgent meeting with the show's producer's first thing on Monday morning to discuss her future.

Vont

"This is news to me", she told us. "I haven't heard anything official because I've been having a few days off. But if this is true, like, then I feel really sad. Not just for me, but for all the viewers who have really

A sombre faced Elizabeth Windsor arrives at the Royal Family studios for work yesterday. Cast members were said to be stunned by the news.

By our Essex Doorstepping Correspondent **KIM SLAPARSE**

taken the Queen Mum to their hearts over the years".

Tres

"I only hope they'll consider leaving the door open for her to return at some point in the future. It would be nice for me to be able to go away and do other things, and still pop back to the Family now and then. To do Christmas specials and that, like what Mike Reid does in EasteEnders", she added.

Bien

But Lizzy's future outside of the soap could be uncertain. After 97 years in the same role

casting directors may see her as stereotyped and she could have trouble finding work. In the past other Family stars have struggled after leaving the show.

Ensemble

Sarah Ferguson was fired after a notorious off-screen toe sucking incident with her boyfriend in 1994. Ferguson, who played red haired man-eater the Duchess of York, has since failed to re-launch her career in Hollywood and is now said to be heavily in debt.

Tres

This winter she is booked to appear alongside Chris Quentin and Peter Dean in Puss In Boots at the Empire Theatre, Bridlington.

But there's no return for Princess Diana

THERE could be even more surprises in store for Family viewers as producers ring in the changes in an attempt to rejuvenate the flagging show.

But producers have so far ruled out a return for Princess Diana, one of the shows most popular characters. Family bosses know that her return would be an enormous coup, but her controversial death in a car crash has left script writers with a headache.

Bien

One way around the problem was for her to return by stepping out of a shower, and for her death and all subsequent events to be explained as a dream. But

producers have dismissed the idea as too far fetched.

Ensemble

However a comeback could be on the cards for Princess Alice of Athlone, grand-daughter of Queen Victoria. Insiders confirm that former Carry On star Joan Simms could be handed the role following the real-life death of veteran actress Margaret Rutherford who played the crotchety Alice for over 80 years.

Letterbocks

"It's the page that can do 5 pop shots in 2 hours"

Letterbocks
PO Box 1PT
Newcastle upon Tyne
NE99 1PT

Fax: 0191 2414244
viz.comic@virgin.net

Nan the wiser

❑ My Nan always used to tell us that you get what you pay for. Well not these days you don't. I bought a porn video called "Under 19s Anal Heaven" from a shop in Nottingham, and the tape turned out to be a chuffing blank.
It's a good job my Nan's dead or she'd be eating her words.

Pol Brun
London SE13

Water good idea

❑ Instead of having droughts, why don't the water companies simply make water when it runs short? As any schoolboy will tell you, the chemical formula is H2O, that is to say two hydrogen molecules for one oxygen molecule. So why not simply mix them together? Two tankers full of hydrogen to one tanker full of oxygen, stir it around it bit, and hey presto. Problem solved, surely.

M.Robinson
Huddersfield

❑ Who was it that said 'out of sight out of mind?' Since I hid my grandmothers spectacles on top of a wardrobe last week she's rarely thought about anything else.

Anthony Wilcock
Chiswick

❑ Jehovah's Witnesses say they don't celebrate Christmas because Jesus was born three months earlier than December. In that case, how come they don't have a piss up on the 25th of September? They're just a bunch of miserable doorstep loitering party poopers.

John Sowerby
Sedbergh, Cumbria

❑ I can sympathise entirely with that poor bloke who went mad after being hypnotised by TV's Paul McKenna. I paid £20 to see one of his shows and I was fucking *furious* by the time I left.

G. L.
Lanarkshire

❑ They say what comes around goes around, or something like that. Well, my uncle refused to fight during the second world war cos he could never bring himself to kill another human being. He was enlisted as an ambulance driver instead, working in London during the Blitz.
On his first day at work he ran into a bus queue and killed 27 people.

Mr S. King
Gateshead

If I wasn't a carpenter...

❑ It seems ironic that Jesus, a carpenter by trade, was killed by being nailed to some wood. If he was a plumber do you suppose they would have drowned him in a toilet?

John Sowerby
Sedburgh, Cumbria

❑ Isn't it an amazing coincidence that all the gobshite TV presenters have the same middle name. Chris Bastard Evans, Terry Bastard Wogan, Noel Bastard Evans, Jeremy Bastard Beadle.
The only exception to the rule is Cilla Fucking Black.

Percy Hedgehog
Bensham, Gateshead

Cilla - yesterday.

Zig-a-zig... car

❑ "Viva forever", sing the Spice Girls. My fucking arse. I bought a brand new one in 1973 and the clutch went after a fortnight.

G. Lambie
Larkhall, Lanarkshire

Pubic service announcement

❑ I wonder if I could use the pages of your magazine to relay a message to Matt Coomber who has been on holiday in Australia for the last six months.
Matt - if you're reading this, phone your mum. She wants to know if you still want all the jazz mags she's just found in your bedroom.

Ian Warren
London

❑ So, the AA are the "fourth emergency service"? Reassuring isn't it. Next time my boat capsizes miles out at sea, I'll remember to call them so that some fat tosser in a yellow van can can come along and arrange to have my car towed away.

L.T.
Wakefield

Fellatious statistic

❑ According to a recent survey, .02% of the male population can suck their own cock. That's hardly a reliable statistic. If I could suck my own cock I don't think I'd have much time for answering questionnaires.

J.S.
Cumbria

❑ I spotted Malcolm out of Modern Parents in my local newspaper. If its not him, they certainly share the same dentist.

Steven Bashforth
Oldham

Semen's rest

❑ On the subject of wanking facilities provided in foreign countries, (Nobby, this page) on a recent trip across the USA I came upon this novel rest area just outside Minneapolis. Americans sure know how to relax.

N. Nosneb
Wheathampstead

❑ 'Drink Australian, think Australian'. So says the current TV ads for the famous antipodean amber nectar. If that's the case, how come we don't see any of the characters portrayed in the ad being deported for stealing, displacing the local ethnic community or shoving their cocks up a kangaroo's arse?

Albert Muffin
Balham

BOOKBINDING CLASS

COME IN. MAKE YOURSELF A TOME.

DOCTOR. I'VE GOT ONE LEG SHORTER THAN THE OTHER

CAN YOU LEND ME A FIVER?

I WAS JUST GOING TO ASK YOU FOR A TENNER

☐ Several weeks ago I sent Denise Van Outen some of my pubic hair and a photocopy of my penis, yet she still hasn't had the decency to reply. Isn't it about time some of these so-called 'celebrities' looked down from their ivory towers and realised that it's borderline psychotics like myself who made them what they are today.

John Sowerby
Sedbergh, Cumbria

Down but not out

☐ Like the previous correspondent's bar one's uncle, my father also refused to fight during the war. As a result he received countless white feathers in the post.
But he had the last laugh. He set up a pillow factory and by the end of the war he was a millionaire.

Malcolm Ard
Kings Cross

☐ Loch Ness monster hunters are wasting their time. No matter what evidence they produce the so-called experts will scoff, and label it a "hoax", a "weather balloon", a "floating log" or an "otter". The monster could dance out of the loch wearing a boater, carrying a cane and singing 'Donald Wear's Ya Troosers' and they'd still say it was a trick of the light.
I think the monster hunters would be better off just staying at home and getting in a few beers in and a Jurassic Park video.

Tommy Take-away
Elgin, Scotland

Game bird

☐ Why all the fuss about the Queen Mum? My gran is in her nineties, drinks pints, rides a Honda 1250 and never misses an issue of Viz. Gawd bless her.

A.C.
Rowlands Gill

Cannon Fodder

From our William Conrad correspondent in L.A. Barracuda Plantagenet Jr.

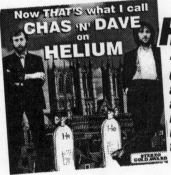
Conrad - ate all the pies

THE SHELVES of pie shops across America were standing empty last night after it was revealed that gargantuan seventies actor William Conrad had ate all the pies.
Scuffles broke out in the early hours over the few remaining pies, but as dawn broke, it became clear that there was no pies left.

Pies

We rang American Pie songwriter Don McClean to ask for a comment, but he said he was Don McClean off Crackerjack.

This year, come to the

Fake District

Britain's best kept tourist secret.

Britain's premier full size replica area of outstanding natural beauty- 10.000 square miles of ersatz hills, valleys & lakes. Stroll down quiet byways to sleepy villages. Situated just 2 minutes from junction 5 of the M42 near Solihull.

For a REAL holiday, it's got to be the Fake District

CHAS 'n' DAVE SING GREGORIAN CHANT...

on HELIUM!

Now THAT'S what I call CHAS 'N' DAVE on HELIUM

"A combination of Cockney Knockabout, ancient Latin texts and light gas surely make this the most unusual record of the year"

Melody Maker

Recorded LIVE at Wells Cathedral

CD.LP
8 Track Cartridge

OUT NOW!!

Top Tips

LIVEN up your tortoise by installing a small solar panel in its shell.
John Tait
Thropton

SLUGS. Always carry salt tablets for emergencies. In the event of a human pouring salt on you, swallowing the tablets will equalise the osmotic effect.
A. E. Millar
Caterham, Surrey

BORED hairdressers. Make your scissors perform a titillating 'Can-Can' show into the mirror by standing them on their tips and then opening and closing them rapidly.
J. Tait
Thropton

VEGGIES. Avoid wearing T shirts that boldly pronounce your vegetarianism. Otherwise everyone will know who it was that farted.
M. J. Worthington
Macclesfield

SHOES will last 20% longer if you increase the length of your stride by one fifth.
Michael Pratt
Sutton

FELLAS. Show your wife who is boss by taking her to a Bruce Springsteen concert.
Michael Pratt
Sutton

PRETEND to be a newsagent by only allowing one of your children into the house at any one time. Then sell them fireworks and cigarettes.
Chris Mappley
Carshalton

UGLY birds. Save a fortune by not going out to the pub until last orders. Let's face it, no-one is going to chat you up until then, so why stand around all evening buying your own drinks?
Chris Mappley
Carshalton

TRIANGULAR plastic sandwich packs make ideal video racks - for one video.
Greg Wigg
Toddington, Glos.

CRIMINALS. Keep constantly changing your genetic fingerprints by holidaying once a year at Sellafield.
A. E. Millar
Caterham, Surrey

WHEN timing a boiled egg by running a four minute mile, remember to turn round half-way, or the egg will be hard-boiled by the time you get back.
M. Wilson
Bridlington

PRACTICAL jokers. Pour a jar of curry sauce into your 'Whoopee' cushion for that realistic 'follow through' effect.
John Tait
Thropton

RECREATE the thrills of a modern swimming pool with water slide by filling your bath with cold water, pouring in 6 bottles of Domestos, then pissing in it. Then saw the bottom off a plastic dustbin, jam it in the bathroom window, then climb up a drainpipe and dive through the dustbin and into the bath. Fun for all the family.
Big Carlos
Inverness

SUNBATHERS. Place two wet tea bags beneath your sunglasses to avoid those dreaded white eye-patches. Hey presto! A perfectly even facial tan.
Penny Taylor
Southwold, Suffolk

ASTRONOMERS. Poppadoms make excellent 'relief' maps of the Moon.
E. A. Browse
Westcliff-on-Sea

A SPUD-GUN loaded from a garlic bulb makes the ideal weapon for killing vampires.
John Tait
Thropton

CREATE your own fleece-lined jogging pants by snipping the feet of a pair of tights and emptying the contents of a Hoover bag down the insides.
John Tait
Thropton

HEAVY smokers. Make yourself think you smoke less by emptying your ashtray at regular intervals.
Nathan-Madonna Byers

LADIES. Always keep a car fan belt in your handbag - just in case your tights snap.
J. T.
Thropton

VICKI DRAKE

VICKI'S BEEN OUT SHOPPING IN THE FULCHESTER SHOPPING MALL...

PUFF PANT! MORE McSEATS UP McSTAIRS!

BUT... GASP!

"FOOD"

LOOKS LIKE ANOTHER FAMILY FEUD TO SORT OUT!

RIGHT SIR, CAN YOU TELL US ALL WHAT YOUR NAME IS?

ER-YEAH- IT'S TOM

RIGHT TIM, FOR THE BENIFIT OF THE RESTAURANT, TELL US OF YOUR BATTLE WITH THE BULDGE-BECAUSE YOU NEED HELP!

WHAT?! AW-C'MON! WE ALL WANT TO KNOW WHAT ITS LIKE TO BE AS DISGUSTINGLY REPELLENTLY UNATTRACTIVE AS YOU BECAUSE OF YOUR OBESITY, DON'T WE?

EH? I'M JUST HAVING A BURGER

AH, BUT ONE BURGER LEADS TO THREE WHICH LEADS TO SEVEN OR EIGHT... TWELVE BURGERS?! TELL ME TIM, H'AVE YOU NEVER HEARD THE PHRASE "NO MORE PLEASE" OR "IAM FULL"? HAVE YOU NEVER HEARD OF DIETING?

WELL- I HAVE DIETED ONCE OR TWICE IN MY LIFE, YES...

ONCE OR TWICE?! LOOK AT YOU! YOU'RE A FAT UGLY HUGE DISGUSTING BLOB! YOU'RE FOUL! IF YOU EAT ANYMORE YOU'LL CRUSH YOURSELF AND DIE!! YOU DO KNOW THAT FAT PEOPLE CAN KILL THEMSELVES DON'T YOU?

ERM- WELL, I HAVE HEARD IT, YES, BUT-

EXCELLENT! ADMITTING YOU'VE A PROBLEM MEANS YOU'RE HALFWAY THERE TO SORTING IT. IT'S ALL DOWNHILL FROM HERE-BUT IT'S NOT GOING TO BE EASY, IT'S GOING TO BE TOUGH, AND I MEAN HARD! BUT THE WEIGHT WILL SOON FLY OFF, IT'S NOTHING- I KNOW, I'VE BEEN THERE.

WORST FOUR YEARS OF MY LIFE

WHAT THE HELL'S GOING ON?

GOD KNOWS. I THINK SHE'S A FUCKING MENTAL! EAT YOUR BURGER, QUICK

AH- YOU MUST BE TIMS WIFE- CONGRATULATIONS, VERY WELL DONE

OH, YOU'RE VERY KIND, THANKYOU

YEAH, IT MUST BE TOUGH LOOKING AFTER THAT LAZY FAT CUNT

GOD- IMAGINE IT, 24 HOURS A DAY, HAND ON FOOT, FOR SOMEONE WHO CAN'T EVEN SWITCH OFF THE T.V. AND GET OFF THE SOFA, LET ALONE FIT OUTSIDE THE FRONT DOOR OF HIS OWN HOUSE

AND IT'S STARTING TO SHOW... YOUR SKIN IS SLIGHTLY WRINKLING, YOUR BOOBS ARE SAGGING, YOUR ARSE IS GETTING HUGE, AND AS FOR YOUR FACE- WELL, OBVIOUSLY YOU'RE NO OIL PAINTING...

WHAT?

Y' FUCKIN' UGLY BITCH

I THINK YOU NEED A MAKEOVER... VICKI STYLE!!

HMM...AND SOME COUNSELLING

BOO HOO HOO!!

SOB SOB SOB! THERE THERE DEAR

FUCK OFF! DON'T TOUCH ME!

EXCUSE ME IS THERE A PROBLEM HERE?

DAMN RIGHT THERES A PROBLEM BUSTER!! WHAT ARE YOU DOING WORKIN' IN THIS SEEDY BURGER BAR? WHEN ARE YOU GOING TO MATURE AND FACE UP TO YOUR RESPONSIBILITIES AND GET A DECENT, RESPECTABLE JOB?

WELL IAM QUITE HAPPY BEING THE MANAGER HERE THANKYOU. ME AND THE WIFE DO VERY COMFORTABLY

UNTILL NOW!! SHE'S BACKSTAGE, WE'RE GONNA BRING HER OUT... ARE YOU READY TO TELL HER YOUR SHOCKING SECRET ABOUT HOW YOU WANK OFF IN THE FILLET OF FISH BEHIND HER BACK?

I THINK YOU BOTH NEED COUNSELLING!

RIGHT, IAM CALLING SECURITY

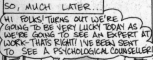

SO, MUCH LATER...

HI FOLKS! TURNS OUT WE'RE GOING TO BE VERY LUCKY TODAY AS WE'RE GOING TO SEE AN EXPERT AT WORK-THATS RIGHT! I'VE BEEN SENT TO SEE A PSYCHOLOGICAL COUNSELLER!

EXCUSE ME- MISS DRAKE?

YES? THE DOCTOR WILL SEE YOU NOW, BUT HE HAS SOME PSYCHOLOGY STUDENTS WITH HIM AT THE MOMENT- WOULD IT BE O.K. IF THEY OBSERVED THE SESSION?

GEE- I GUESS SO

SO... WELCOME TO THE SESSION MISS DRAKE, PLEASE- TAKE A SEAT

THANKYOU- I KNOW I'VE COME TO THE RIGHT PLACE

SCRAPE!

AND THE SUBJECT OF TODAYS SESSION- "HELP! I THINK IAM A TALK SHOW HOST!!"

YEAH! WOO! HE NO GOOD SISTER! FINISH HIM GIRL!

WOO! FIGHT!

VICKI!

TER-RY! TER-RY! TER-RY!

WOO!

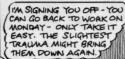

Dawson watch

Comic Les's ghostly image appears in Di funeral snap

A year after the funeral of Diana, Princess of Wales, it has emerged than a host of dead celebrities may have turned up to pay their last respects.

Lonely obsessive Frank Dismal has been closely examining photographs of the funeral since he stumbled on an eerie image of Les Dawson formed by a tree's leaves in one blurred picture of the funeral cortege. The figure, which is unmistakably that of the late roly poly funnyman, appears to be looking over the crowds of mourners as Diana's coffin passes by.

Teeth

But some cynics have not been impressed with his remarkable photo. "Les is in character, dressed as a woman with no teeth, and is wearing rollers and a hair net. So he isn't immediately recognisable. But once you do see him, the likeness is quite scary. Even now the hairs on the back of my neck stand up every time I look at it".

Economy

Frank, who has never had a girlfriend, spotted the eerie image as soon as his pictures came back from the chemist, but chose to wait until the first anniversary of Diana's death before going public.

Ceiling

"But its also nice to think that a big hearted star like Les would go out of his way to be there for Diana's funeral, despite being dead himself", Frank continued.

Hips

Since spotting Les's unmistable features, Frank believes he has identified up to a dozen other dead showbusiness stars peering out of the trees, among them Jimi Hendrix, Elvis Presley, Sid James, Judy Garland and former Dixon of Dock Green actor Jack Warner. And in another shot of the family mourners Frank noticed Richard Burton peering out the folds in the Duke of Edinburgh's trousers.

Snap! Frank's pic (right) contains an unmistakable image of Les, enlarged below.

Can you see the hidden celebrity spooks paying their last re*spectres*?

How many grieving ghouls can you see hidden in this tree? We've hidden the eerie images of five famous folks, all of whom are dead, in this tree and imagined that they have turned up in spirit form to pay their last respects at the funeral of Diana, Princess of Wales. Can you spot the lot? View this page in a mirror and the ghouls names will eerily appear in the box below....

Hughie Green, Richard Dimbleby, Noel Gordon, Dick Emery, Peter Cook

A MUST FOR EVERY HOUSE PROUD MASS MURDERER

Fred West's guide to FENG SHUI

Make your home into a Happy House of Horrors with the ancient Chinese art of Feng Shui. Britain's top mass murderer the late Fred West looks *East* for inspiration in this innovative, illustrated guide to interior design.

COPING WITH CORPSES - and their karma

HOW TO BURY THOSE BAD VIBES - in the cellar

DEAD SPACE - and how to use it

A MASS MURDERER'S GUIDE TO FENG SHUI
FRED WEST

BUILDING THE PERFECT, PEACEFUL PATIO - overnight!

CHANNELLING THAT CHI - through your alcoves, attic and wall cavities

"If I'd had this book 10 Rillington Place could have been a palace".
John Christie

"With advice like this I would never have blocked all them drains".
Dennis Neilsen

ON SALE NOW from DIY stores and HMSO bookshops priced £10.99

A First Anniversary Commemoration of Diana, Princess of Wales
The *Full English Breakfast Plate* of Hope

100% of the profits from sales of this plate will go to causes close to Diana's heart. Like messing about on yachts in the Mediterranean, and extravagant shopping sprees in London, Paris and New York.

Plate shown smaller than actual size. The woeful quality of reproduction here is clearly on a par with what you can expect to find on the actual plate.

It was a morning when none of us could face our breakfast, and fifty million fried eggs went uneaten as a nation united in grief.

Sergio Clitoris

As the news spread thousands of ordinary people dropped their knives and forks and travelled from all corners of the country to pay their respects outside the gates of Kensington Palace. And behind them they left a sea of unfinished breakfasts.

Since that day many have been unable to face a fried breakfast. But now comes an opportunity to regain our appetites with this, the *Diana Memorial Full English Breakfast Plate of Hope*.

Renowned cash-in plate artist *Sergio Clitoris* has taken the striking image of the English Breakfast and used it to capture the essence of our English Rose on this unique, catering quality heirloom edition collector's plate. Through bacon the artist lovingly acknowledges Diana's sizzling looks, and the streak of kindness we all came to know. Two sausages symbolise her two lives, private and public, short but into which this thin skinned woman stuffed so much. The tomato - her heart - big and red, with pips denoting the time she had for others. And the egg itself, Diana, soft on the inside, always sunny side up, smiling through her personal heartache. And finally, a small portion of grilled mushrooms reminds us how 'mushroom' she had for us in her heart.

You can view the *Full English Breakfast of Hope* in your own home for up to 7 days, on condition that you buy it. Simply fill in and return the legally binding no-obligation order form opposite.

About the artist
Sergio Clitoris was born in Wolverhampton in 1978 where his father was a train guard. In 1995 he received a Grade 4 CSE in Art from Tipton College of Further Education and his work features prominently in collections across Europe and the USA, notably in Happy Eater and Little Chef.

RESERVATION ORDER FORM

The *Full English Breakfast Plate* of Hope

To: Silverfish & Woodlouse, Laybye House, A464 Eastbound, Wolverhampton.

Please send me the *Full English Breakfast Plate of Hope*. I am labouring under the mistaken impression that the price is £29.99 and I will be billed prior to despatch of my plate.

Name _____

Address _____
_____

To order your Full English Breakfast Plate cut out this form and hang it on your front door before 3.30am.

A small postage, packing and delivery insurance charge of £95 will be added to your bill.

Medieval Knievel

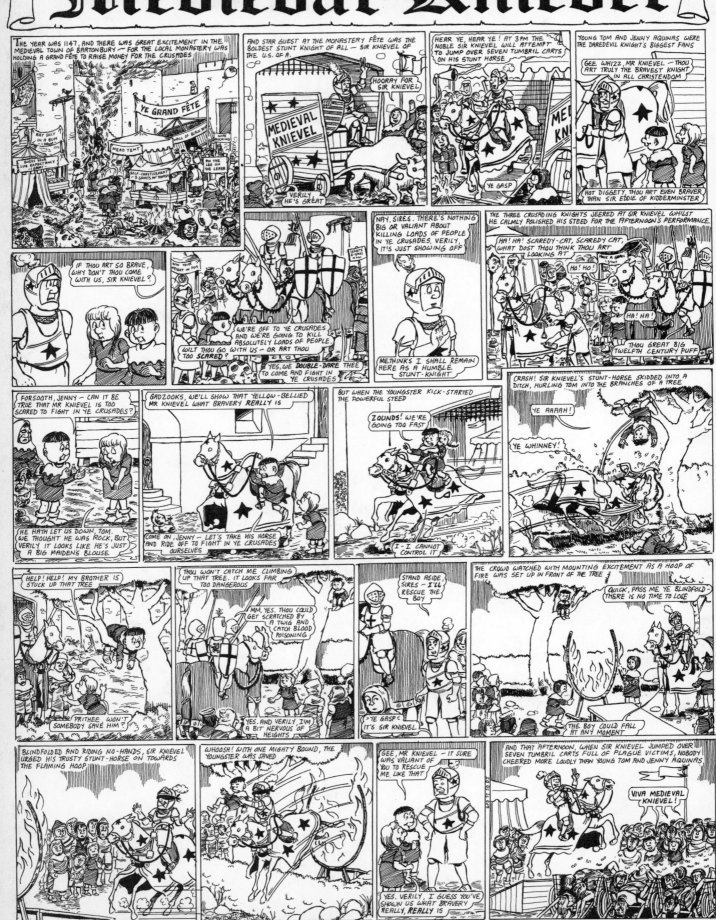

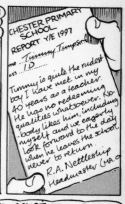

HEIR INDOORS

'No' to open door policy at Palace

AN urgent enquiry is to be launched after Prince Charles was left stranded inside a Buckingham Palace drawing room for almost 3 days last weekend.

By our Royal Correspondent Lickanarse Owen

The distressed Prince was found in a puddle of his own urine early on Monday morning by Palace cleaning staff.

Lunch

Charles is thought to have entered the small drawing room through an open door at around midday on Friday whilst visiting his mother the Queen for lunch. But when the door blew shut behind him, the Prince found himself alone inside the room.

Snuff

Palace staff who would normally open doors for the Prince failed to check the room before going off duty for the weekend and

Prisoner in the Palace - Charles wet himself

were unaware of the future King's plight.

Cardboard

Charles was discovered at 5am on Monday morning by cleaning staff who had gone to the room to puff up cushions. He was reported to be in a distressed state, wandering around in circles and fiddling with his cuffs. The room was said to stink of faeces and urine.

Black

"Protocol has always forbidden members of the Royal Family opening doors for themselves", explained Royal author Sir Terrapin Walnut-Cake. "Charles would be totally baffled if confronted by a door which was closed. It would be a situation totally alien to a man of his upbringing and pedigree".

Robbie

The last monarch to open a door for himself was Henry VIII who caused a storm in 1545 by famously opening a bathroom cabinet in order to get some Alka Seltzer late at night.

Juke

Nowadays for security reasons all Royals are told never to enter a room on their own unless the door is securely fastened in an open position, or they can see an alternative exit. But it is thought that Charles, who has a stubborn streak, may have deliberately ignored this advice whilst going for a stroll.

The Prince of Wales spent Monday morning undergoing tests in a private room at St James' hospital in London. He was visited by his brother Edward who brought him clean underwear and some new trousers.

Dirt

Charles was later allowed home to Highgrove, and paused briefly to joke with a small crowd of demented old women and jingoistic, bigoted taxi drivers as he left the hospital.

DESPITE this latest scare the Queen remains reluctant to break hundreds of years of Royal tradition by allowing members of the Royal Family to open doors for themselves.

In 1982 Prince Edward risked the wrath of his mother by taking secret door opening lessons while studying at Gordonstoun school. However it was the Queen Mother who put a stop to it, threatening to turn Edward into a frog if the lessons continued.

Signs

But there are signs that in the Post Diana era the Royals are at least beginning to start to perhaps recognise the need for possible change.

Seals

The legacy of Diana is that Wills and Harry are able to use a TV remote control, and perhaps significantly, both princes wave to the public with an open hand, as opposed to the traditional rotating wrist 'wanker' style gesture preferred by the Queen.

Delivers

Haughty Royal nanny Threepotsandin Legless-Burke was recently scolded by Charles after photographs of Princes

Unhinged - Queen slams door on Royal door opening

Queen Mum - God Bless Her, she's 98 you know - made frog threats.

Harry and William opening a car door themselves during a holiday in Wales appeared in Sunday newspapers. But after his own harrowing experience it is hoped that Charles' attitude towards door opening may soften.

A snip at £40,000

A spokesman for the Royal Society of Gentlemen's Hairdressers yesterday defended the enormous hair cutting bill which Prince Charles has received after his two sons visited the barbers in July. He described the £40,000 bill as "not unusual".

Haircut

Former Prime Minister John Major took the boys, William and Harry, for a haircut at exclusive Mayfair barbers Shirtlift & Poovery over a month ago. However the Prince of Wales was said to be shocked by the size of the bill which he received several weeks later.

100

"The account no doubt reflects the amount of time that must have been spent on these haircuts, and it also includes a shampoo and rinse", said the spokesman whilst struggling to keep a straight face.

Rude GARDENERS' QUESTION TIME

With 'The Rude Gardener'

Dear Rude Gardener
Last year I planted a rhododendron but it has failed to flower and now it looks quite sickly. Everything else in the garden is fine. What could be wrong?
Mrs B., Essex

* *You should have tested your fucking soil, you twat. They grow best in **acidic** soil, not lime, you dozy bitch. You've wasted your money and my fucking time. Next.*

Dear Rude Gardener
Is it possible to grow olive trees outdoors in England?
Mr A. Kelly, Birmingham

* *Is it fuck.*

Dear Rude Gardener
On holiday recently in Devon I spotted a small yellow flower with white stripes on the petals and distinctive heart shaped leaves. I would very much like to grow it in my garden but do not know its name. Have you any idea what this pretty flower might have been?
Mrs Mary Hetherington

* *How the fuck should I know? I didn't see it.*

Send your queries to the Rude Gardener c/o Viz. The Rude Gardener regrets that he is far too busy to enter into individual correspondence with the likes of you. So fuck off.

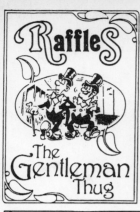

VINCE & POLLY
"TIE THE KNOT"

IF ANY PERSON HERE PRESENT KNOWS OF ANY REASON WHY THIS COUPLE MAY NOT BE JOINED IN HOLY MATRIMONY, THEN LET THEM SPEAK NOW, OR FOREVER HOLD THEIR PEACE.

A-HEM!!...

...AM I TO TAKE IT, THEREFORE, THAT IF I KNOW OF AN IMPEDIMENT, WHICH WOULD NULIFY THE SOLEMNISATION OF THIS CONTRACT, LET US SAY THAT THE BRIDE WERE THE GROOM'S BROTHER'S DECEASED SON'S WIDOW, PURSUANT TO THE MARRIAGE ACT OF 1836, THAT I WOULD NOT BE LEGALLY REQUIRED TO DISCLOSE SAID INFORMATION TO THE REGISTRAR?

SURELY THEN, THE MARRIAGE, EVEN UPON MY SILENCE, WOULD BE A CRIMINAL ACT, TO WHICH I WOULD BE A PARTY.

FURTHERMORE, WHAT IF A PRESENTLY UNKNOWN IMPEDIMENT PRESENTS ITSELF TO ME AT SOME POINT IN THE FUTURE, THIS SUBJECT MATTER IS NOT COVERED AT ALL IN YOUR STATEMENT.

WHAT!? WHAT?! IS THIS TRUE? DID YOU HEAR THAT?! SHE'S SOMEBODY'S WIDOW'S BROTHER OR SOMETHING? WHAT?! ALREADY MARRIED? I KNEW SHE WAS NO GOOD.

MAY I SUGGEST THAT A FAR LESS EQUIVOCAL COUCHING OF THE PERTINENT PREMISES WOULD BE AS FOLLOWS, "ANY PERSON WHO KNOWS, OR SUBSEQUENTLY ASCERTAINS INFORMATION WHICH COULD LEAD TO A DISOLUTION OF THE MATRIMONIAL CONTRACT IS REQUIRED BY LAW TO: a) INFORM THE REGISTRAR DIRECTLY, OR b) INFORM THE REGISTRAR AND THE POLICE DIRECTLY, OR AT YOUR EARLIEST OPPORTUNITY, AND IN AN EVENT, WITHIN 24 HOURS OF DISCLOSURE...

...ALL SAID BEING EFFECTIVE WITHOUT CONSTRAINT OF TIME OR VITALITY OF EITHER PARTNER"

ERM... HAVE YOU GOT THE RING? I HAVE A RING.

YES... ERM, COULD YOU GIVE ME IT? I COULD.

ERM... WOULD YOU GIVE IT TO ME? I WOULD, IF INSTRUCTED TO DO SO.

I DON'T UNDERSTAND. WHY AREN'T YOU GIVING ME THE RING? YOU WERE MERELY INQUIRING ABOUT THE POSSIBILITY OF THE RING'S TRANSFER.

LOOK! JUST GIVE ME THE FUCKING RING!

OF COURSE, HERE IS THE RING, AS YOU REQUESTED.

NOW... IF THE GROOM WOULD PLACE THE RING ON THE THIRD FINGER OF...

A-HEM!

IN ORDER TO COUNT THE FINGERS UP TO A GIVEN NUMBER, A STARTING POINT MUST FIRST BE ESTABLISHED. THE CLASSIFICATION OF THUMBS ALSO COMES INTO QUESTION...

LATER...

SPEECH! SPEECH!

CIVIC HALL

POLLY AND VINCE RECEPTION

I HAVE STUDIED MY DUTIES AS A BEST MAN THOROUGHLY AND SYSTEMATICALLY AND HAVE DISCOVERED IT TO BE CUSTOMARY FOR ME TO BEGIN MY SPEECH WITH ONE OR TWO HUMOROUS ASIDES. I HAVE WRITTEN TWO, THUS...

1) WHAT IS THE DIFFERENCE BETWEEN A GNU AND A GNOSTIC?

A GNU IS A LARGE AFRICAN ANTELOPE, AND A GNOSTIC IS A PHILOSOPHER OF THE 1st CENTURY A.D., WHOSE DOCTRINES WERE A MIXTURE OF ANCIENT MYTHOLOGY, EASTERN BELIEFS AND THE JEWISH AND CHRISTIAN RELIGIONS.

2) DID YOU HEAR ABOUT THE IRISH HYGROMETER? IT DIDN'T KNOW HOW TO MEASURE THE MOISTNESS OF THE ATMOSPHERE.

I HAVE KNOWN VINCE FOR 14·85333 RECURRING YEARS UP TO 11am. THIS MORNING. I HAVE KNOWN THE BRIDE, WHO'S NAME ESCAPES ME, FOR 8·324 YEARS, AS INDEED HAS THE AFOREMENTIONED GROOM.

I REMEMBER WELL THE EVENING THEY MET. MARCH 23rd 1990, IN A NIGHTCLUB CALLED MR. VITONI'S. THEY BECAME FIRM FRIENDS IMMEDIATELY.

IN FACT THEY PROCEEDED TO SPEND THE NIGHT TOGETHER, ENGAGING IN SEVERAL SEXUAL ACTS; PETTING, HEAVY PETTING, MUTUAL MASTURBATION, ORAL GENITAL CONTACT, AND CULMINATING IN VAGINAL PENETRATION. THIS INFORMATION WAS DISCLOSED TO ME THE FOLLOWING MORNING BY VINCE, WHO THEN EXPRESSED A CONCERN THAT HIS EJACULATED SEMEN IN POLLY'S VAGINA COULD LEAD TO AN UNWANTED PREGNANCY, AS NO FORM OF CONTRACEPTION WAS USED TO HIS KNOWLEDGE.

SNACK!

I CALCULATED THE CHANCE OF PREGNANCY FROM A SINGLE INTRO-LABIAL SEMINAL DISCHARGE AS BEING 123-1. WHICH LEADS ME ON TO STATISTICS. TAKING INTO ACCOUNT AGE OF BOTH PARTIES, LENGTH OF COURTSHIP, PREVIOUS FIDELITY RECORDS; FOR INSTANCE VINCE HAS HAD SEXUAL INTERCOURSE WITH ELEVEN WOMEN TO MY COGNIZANCE – INCLUDING THE BRIDE'S SISTER AND MOTHER – THEY HAVE AN 88% CHANCE OF DIVORCE WITHIN THE FIRST TWELVE MONTHS OF MARRIAGE.

THUD!

SO IT ONLY REMAINS FOR ME TO PROPOSE A TOAST TO THE HAPPY COUPLE AND WISH THEM ALL THE BEST IN THEIR LIFE TOGETHER...

...THE BRIDE AND GROOM!

98

Grassy Knollington

CONSPIRACY THEORIST

OH BOTHER - I MUST HAVE LEFT ONE OF YOUR RED SOCKS IN THE WASHING MACHINE, GRASSY. EVERYTHING'S GONE PINK.

WHAT?! LET ME SEE THAT SOCK.

IT DOESN'T MATTER. IT WAS MY FAULT - I'LL JUST STICK IT ALL IN SOME BLEACH.

SOCKS DON'T JUST "GET LEFT" IN THE WASHING MACHINE. THEY'RE PUT THERE ...AS PART OF A SINISTER GLOBAL CONSPIRACY...

...AND YOU'RE THE PATSY!

I DON'T KNOW ABOUT THAT, GRASSY, BUT YOUR DAD'LL BE CROSS IF HIS PANTS ARE ALL PINK.

HMM... I JUST DON'T BUY THIS "LONE SOCK" THEORY.

NO SIGN OF A BREAK-IN. SO WHOEVER PLANTED THE SOCK HAD ACCESS TO KEYS.

HMM! THIS IS A BARRATT HOUSE !...SO...THE ONLY OTHER PERSON WHO WOULD HAVE KEYS IS... SIR LAWRIE BARRATT!

THIS CALLS FOR MORE INVESTIGATION.

LET ME SEE NOW... LAWRIE BARRATT - KNIGHTED BY THE QUEEN IN 1982 ... SO SHE'S INVOLVED IN THIS AS WELL!

HMM... IF A=1, B=2, C=3 etc. THE LETTERS IN "RED SOCK" ADD UP TO 75, THE LETTERS IN "QUEEN" ADD UP TO 62. TAKE 62 FROM 75 AND YOU GET... 13...

...THE NUMBER OF THE PILLAR LADY DI'S CAR CRASHED INTO!

WOW! THIS THING GOES EVEN DEEPER THAN I THOUGHT.

TAP TAPPITY TAP...

NEXT DAY...

PSSST! MUM!

WHAT IS IT, GRASSY?

BATHROOM

IN HERE. QUICK!

WHAT ARE YOU DOING?

SSSH!...WE'RE PROBABLY BEING LISTENED TO...

SPLOSH!

I'VE WORKED IT OUT! IT ALL BEGINS AT THE TIME OF THE CRUSADES. THE KNIGHTS TEMPLAR FIND THE HOLY GRAIL, FOLLOWING DIRECTIONS ENCODED IN THE MEASUREMENTS OF THE GREAT PYRAMID OF CHEOPS. LEONARDO DA VINCI FINDS OUT, LEAVING CLUES AS TO ITS WHERE-ABOUTS HIDDEN IN THE TURIN SHROUD...

TURIN - WHERE THE WHITE FIAT UNO WHICH FORCED PRINCESS DIANA'S CAR OFF THE ROAD WAS MANUFACTURED! BUT I DIGRESS...

FAST FORWARD TO NEW MEXICO. THE CIA, TRYING TO DRAW PUBLIC ATTENTION FROM THE GRAIL, HYPNOTISE MARILYN MONROE TO SHOOT JFK - AND STAGE THE ROSWELL INCIDENT ON THE SAME HOLLYWOOD SET WHERE THEY FAKED THE MOON LANDINGS.

... BUT THAT'S BY THE BY.

ALSO IN THE PRESIDENTIAL LIMOUSINE IS SENATOR JOHN CONNALLY - ARCH ENEMY OF CHICAGO CRIME BOSS (AND FRIEND OF JACK RUBY) - SANTO TRAFFICANTE, A STAUNCH CATHOLIC - LIKE JOHN LENNON, BADGEMAN, AND - SURPRISE SURPRISE! - THE POPE. ANYWAY - BACK TO PARIS, 31st AUGUST, 1997...

SIX HOURS LATER...

...REVEALING THE THIRD SECRET OF FATIMA, AND IS SO SCARED THAT HE SAYS THE BALL HAS GONE OVER THE LINE - AND ENGLAND GO ON TO WIN 4-2 ! SOUNDS FAMILIAR? YOU BET! ELVIS "DIES" AGED 42 - ONLY THEY MIS-SPELL HIS MIDDLE NAME ON THE GRAVE...

ANOTHER SIX HOURS LATER...

...IS BILL CLINTON, A MASON, LIKE JACK THE RIPPER, WHO, IN LEAGUE WITH THE ANCIENT ROSACRUCIANS "THE ORDER OF THE ROSY CROSS" - SET THE WHOLE THING UP. DON'T YOU SEE? "CROSS" - LIKE DAD WAS WHEN HIS PANTS WENT PINK - OR AS THE FRENCH SAY - "ROSE" !?

...AND THAT'S WHY THE SOCK WAS PUT IN THE WASHER.

THAT'S NICE DEAR. ANYWAY - I'LL HAVE TO PUT THE TEA ON NOW.

...AND IT'S ME NEXT. THESE PEOPLE WILL STOP AT NOTHING. I'VE GOT TO GET SOMEWHERE PUBLIC WHERE THE NEW WORLD ORDER WON'T TRY ANYTHING! I'M GOING TO TRAFALGAR SQUARE.

WELL, TEA WILL BE ABOUT ½ AN HOUR.

SHORTLY...

GOD! I SHOULD HAVE LEFT IT ALONE. I'LL NEVER BE SAFE...

...I'LL NEVER BE ABLE TO TRUST ANYONE. I'LL ALWAYS BE LOOKING OVER MY SHOULDER.

NWO

HOLY GRAIL

THIS KID IS CLOSING IN ON US. ARRANGE FOR ONE OF THOSE PIGEONS TO SHIT ON HIS HEAD.

RIGHT AWAY, MR. PRESIDENT.

LetterBox

STATE of NORTH BORNEO
ONE CENT
DORCHESTER
22 A... 198...
DORSE...

Letterbocks,
P.O. Box 1PT,
Newcastle upon
Tyne, NE99 1PT

Fax:
(0191) 2414244
email: viz.comic
@virgin.net

Merry Christmas pal,
*from the page that stinks of piss
and wants ten pence
for a cup of tea.*

What's the Big Ikea?

❑ I think suppliers of crap British flat-pack furniture should advertise with the slogan "Don't be so Swedish" and illustrate it with clips of Swedes hanging themselves, supplying arms to the Nazis and wanking over farmyard animal pornography.

**J. Terry
Hebburn**

Space Age Pensioner

Kirk - ninety

❑ Why all the fuss about John Glenn being the oldest man to go into space? It's all a load of bollocks. Captain Kirk still boldly goes there and he must be nearing fucking ninety

**I. Camel
Saudi Arabia**

❑ I am just writing to say how appalled I will be at the glut of tacky memorabilia which will be produced in the wake of the Queen Mother's death. It will ill befit her memory, everything from tea towels to key rings. The manufacturers of this stuff will ought to be ashamed of themselves.

**G. Grahams
Hove**

❑ I'm as liberal as the next man, and I've got nothing against them personally, but I really don't think it's a good idea for the Prime Minister to fill his cabinet full of gays. The last thing Mr. Blair wants as he sits there with his finger on the nuclear button is Nick Brown and Chris Smith wandering up behind him and stroking his hair.

**T. Kavanagh
Wapping**

❑ I had to laugh the other day. I was sniffing nitrous oxide.

**T. Paddock
Sedbergh**

GERMAN SAUSAGE FACTORY →

LOOKS LIKE HE'S TAKEN A TURN FOR THE WURST

STEVE OLIVE

The Best of Both Miss Worlds

Best and a Miss World he was banging in 1977

❑ I saw on the telly the other day that they have managed to successfully clone sheep, and that human cloning is now a realistic possibility for the future.
Just imagine the world a few years from now, whole armies of eight foot tall soldiers to defend our nations. And what about sport? A whole football team of George Bests! Mind you the problem would be that you'd have to clone eleven ex-Miss Worlds as well, just to keep their nads serviced.

**B. Bingley
Bradford**

Flatley yesterday

❑ On the end of his telly advert for "Feet of Flames", stiff-armed dancer Michael Flatley says "If I never did another show, I would die a happy man". Me too, Mr. Flatley.

**L. Charms
Tadcaster**

❑ Having worked for many years in the tropical diseases department of a large teaching hospital, I have seen first hand the terrible effects of water bourne diseases that wreak havoc on the digestive system. Having said that, I had to laugh when I heard that Esther Rantzen had got amoebic dysentry.

**Dr. C.N. Cornflakes
Battersea**

Fraud of the Dance

Flatley yesterday again

❑ Why does everyone make such a fuss about Michael Flatley and his Riverdancing. There's nothing clever about dancing if you've only got to think about moving your feet. Proper dancers like Lionel Blair wave their arms all over the shop. I think Mr. Flatley should charge half as much as he does for his tickets

**Mrs. H. N. Loops
Rhyl**

Genie with the Light Brown Ale

❑ Last Tuesday, while sat on a park bench drinking Special Brew from a bottle, a Genie appeared and offered me 3 wishes. I wished to be sick, become incontinent and get arrested. Imagine my surprise the next morning on waking up in a police cell to find that all 3 wishes had come true.

**T. Paddock
Millthrop**

Bashing the bishops

❑ What an absolute disgrace the Church of England is. I saw a real bishop's hat the other day, and it was just a piece of cardboard with some cloth glued to it. It was rubbish. Come on Britain's bishops, let's make your hats be the envy of the world once more.

**S. Wheat.
Dorchester**

❑ Week after week, whilst flicking through "Hello" magazine, I am horrified at the state of the electrical wiring in the homes of celebrities. Being in the public eye, they have a duty to set an example, particularly to young people. Surely with all their money, the stars could find some way of powering their appliances which didn't involve trailing mains leads down the backs of tables, across carpets, and along skirting boards.

**D. Pin
Cork**

Bottom of the Pops

❑ Remember that shite song 'If You Ever' with East 17 and Gabrielle? The first line went "The very first time I saw your brown eyes." Because Gabrielle wears that stupid eye patch, the first line *should* have been "The very first time I saw your brown eye," which changes the atmosphere of the song entirely. I'd like to have seen the video to **that** one.

**Rob Ellis
Birmingham**

❑ In the bible, why do they always use a capital 'H' on He or Him or His, when refering to God even if it's in the middle of a sentence? Does he get annoyed if you spell it with a little 'h', like I just have, and if so, what's He going to do about it?

**R. Brek
Kidderminster**

❑ What a lot of nonsense is talked about being run over by buses. My grandfather was run over by his first bus when he was 12- and he was run over 80 times a day until he was 104, when he was killed by a cigarette.

G. Nuggets
Warrington

Excretingly Good Cakes

❑ Whilst reading my German daily paper today, I did a double-take on seeing this picture of an Afghan merchant selling (or trying to sell) goods imported from Iran.

Michael Kirsch
Goppingen

Flatley yesterday once more

❑ In reply to Mrs Loops letter (this issue). What she fails to realise is that although Michael Flatley only moves his legs, they actually go three times faster than Lionel Blair's. This means that his tickets are actually two thirds the price that they ought to be.

Mr. Frosties
Luton

❑ So the EU is clamping down on Suicidal Syds by ruling that no more than 16 paracetamols can be bought at one time. The next thing you know, they'll be ruling that rope can only be bought in 1 metre lengths.

G. Lewis
Abadare

Booze at Ten

❑ ITV bosses' plans to move the News at Ten to an earlier evening slot with an 11 o'clock summary is sheer fucking madness. How will the poor newsreader, get a drink inside him. He'll have to stay sober to read the summary, and then he's missed last orders. Not only that, but he'll have to phone his wife up every night and tell her he's working late. Meanwhile, at the BBC, Michael Burke gets a good two hours drinking in, and Martyn Lewis hits the bar at half past six, the jammy cunt.

T. MacDonald
ITN

❑ I've just been struck by an enormous bolt of lightning. I'm covered in boils and my house is full of frogs. I strongly recommend that when referring to God, always use upper case 'H' on all personal pronouns.

R. Brek
Kidderminster

❑ When I was young, the old folks' uniform was a trilby hat, dark overcoat, a dark suit with baggy trousers and a pair of stiff, shiny, lace-up shoes. Nowadays all coffin dodgers shuffle around dressed head to foot in beige. They look like ghosts even before they're dead.

S. K.
Mansfield

TOP TIPS

FELLAS. Recycle those tired jazzmags by cutting your favourite pictures into head, chest, leg and arm sections. You can then 'mix and match' to create your own 'Wankenstein' beauties.

D. Stocks.
Ipswitch.

A GLASS pudding bowl placed upside down on a lawn makes an ideal 'Centre Parcs' style holiday destination for ants.

Neil
Heaton

FRUIT and veg sellers. Don't throw away damaged oranges. A Capri-Sun orange drink makes an ideal ready-made saline drip with which to get them fit for sale again.

Alex
Upton

MAKE your own swarm of giant bluebottles, by simply smearing bumblebees with Immac.

John Tait
Thropton

OWNERS of carpet tiles. Pretend one of your carpet tiles has anti-gravity by leaping in the air every time you step on it.

Giles T'Ardenflesche
Kensington

BRIDES to be. Have your wedding at a spiritualist church. That way you can have a star studded celebrity guest list. Marilyn Monroe, Elvis Presley and John Lennon could all be invited. Jesus himself could take the service and Red Rum could pull your wedding carriage.

Noel Armstrong
Lancaster

AVOID paying extra for cameras with expensive 'dateback' features by holding a small digital clock at arm's length so it appears in the bottom corner of every photograph.

P. Lepki
Cyberspace

NEVER buy a portable television from a man in the street who's out of breath.

A. Berry
Grimsby.

STEVEN Berkoff. Make a small fortune appearing in Hollywood blockbusters as a stereotypical English baddy. This money will fund your theatre career, treading the boards in front of the very people you've portrayed as scum to a global audience.

A. Dean
Kingston

A PIECE of string and a jammy dodger makes a cheap but effective yo-yo. Leave in the sun for a bit, to give that fashionable 'clutch' effect.

Alex
Rowlands Gill

SAVE pounds at Xmas by turning your kids into Jehovah's Witnesses, eliminating the need to buy them presents. Spend the extra cash you have on fags and booze for a really great Xmas.

L.B.
Bidston

CHRISTMAS ST★R FILE

How will you be spending this Christmas?
We always make a point of having a simple family Christmas at my absolutely massive house in Devon. We all go to church on Christmas morning to thank God for all the helicopters and cars He has blessed us with.

What do you have for Christmas Dinner?
Because we're so rich, a turkey isn't big enough, so we have an elephant with an ostrich stuck up its arse and all the trimmings.

What is the worst present you have ever received?
I remember it well. My parents bought me a shiny red bike when I was 10. I was so disappointed, I cried all day. I had set my heart on a bag of gold.

What is the best present you have ever received?
Three years ago, my wife said to me "I had a problem fitting your present under the tree, so you'd better come outside". And when I went out, there was the biggest bag of fifty-pound notes she had ever given me for Christmas. It was a very emotional moment for both of us.

NOEL EDMONDS
Host of Noel's Christmas House Party

What would you most like to receive this Christmas?
When you've got as much as I have, there are few things left to want. But I would like a full-size railway that ran around the estate, with a solid gold steam engine stoked with diamonds as big as your fist.

Watch in bewilderment as the world accelerates into the distance...

OVER YOUR HEAD

Computer

MAGAZINE — Dec 1998 £2.99

This is the future - and there's no place for you!

It's too LATE!

P5 SD-B+ SuperSocket 7 100Mhz Bus

REVIEWED

- and it may as well be in fucking Chinese.

YOU CAN NEVER **HOPE** TO CATCH UP

FREE CD-ROM

WORTH £39.99

ON THIS DISC- FOUR GREAT PROGRAMS!

1 Something that will jam your mouse solid and make it impossible to switch your computer off.

2 Essential expansion LanDesk native executable command batching DriveMapper and disc defragmenter v3.2 - just what you've always wanted.

3 Several nasty viruses package including The Hong Kong Worm, Data Eater 98 and RAM-fucker 2

4 Top 10 game demos- they're on this disc but you'll never find them

A WORLD of interactive entertainment, tantalisingly close but completely denied to you

Motherboard Megatests!

We look at the Dotlink Magnum II-333 MX

- why don't you just put the kettle on?

IT'S KID'S STUFF

- she's 8, and she's forgotten more than you'll ever know

www.com.rip.van/winkle

OUT NOW

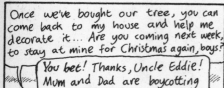

And this is just the start of our Action Group's campaign of liberation... We'll have another surprise for you when you get home from school...

Later....

Ah, you're back, Tarquin... Go and look in your room...

What have you been up to?

AAH!! GOBBLE GOBBLE GOBBLE

GOBBLE GOBBLE

GOBBLE

We liberated them from an animal Auschwitz this afternoon...

It was so exciting!.. The farmer nearly came round the back of the shed when we were getting them into the van!

GOBBLE GOBBLE

Aren't you proud of us, Tarquin? We're at the cutting edge of the eco-freedom-fighter movement!

They've pooed all over my bed!

And one of them's pecked all the Christmas presents I'd bought! Look! This Action Man I got for Guin is ruined!

Tarquin, these are sensitive, peace-loving creatures... They have an instinctive aversion to toys which glorify militarism.

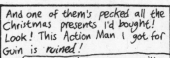

You're mad! I'm glad me and Guin are going to Uncle Eddie's for Christmas.

You won't be going there... We've decided not to let you two see Edward anymore. He's a bad influence on you.

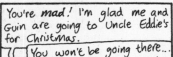

No way!! That's not fair!!

See, you're becoming aggressive... You need to come outside and let the trees help you find your centre...

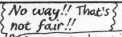

I'll bring the turkeys... We can start helping them learn to fly again so that they can migrate back to their natural habitat in the rainforests of Turkey.

GOBBLE GOBBLE GOBBLE

Come on! Spread your wings! Take to the sky! You're free now!

Maybe they've been too traumatized to ever be returned to the wild... Perhaps we should look for caring homes for them.

Excuse me!

I was just passing and I noticed your fine flock of turkeys... I wonder if any of them are available?

Gosh! Well yes, they all are really, if we can be sure they're going to good homes... They're freed birds, you see.

Excellent! I've plenty of friends and quality customers who really appreciate a free-range bird... Now, how much d'you want? Shall I say a hundred quid for the lot?

Oh...well.. yes, I suppose we should be charging an administration fee to support the running costs of our sanctuary.

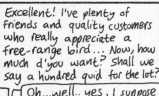

That was a stroke of luck!

Yes, it really restores one's faith in humanity... Hey, maybe we could start an Adopt-a-Tree scheme too!

I. CHOP & SONS QUALITY BUTCHER

The next day....

LIVING CONIFERS Take a tree into your home for just £10.99

Later....

It's been so encouraging! We've only one or two trees left to be placed...

DING DONG

Ah, that'll be another tree-adopter...

Malcolm and Cressida Wright-Pratt?... I am arresting you for breaking and entering, for the theft of 24 Christmas trees and 16 turkeys and for selling stolen goods.

Christmas Day....

Poor old Cressida and Malcolm... Still, I suppose even in prison they'll get some sort of Christmas...

Sister prisoners! As fellow victims of the patriarchal prison authorities, I'm sure, like me, you resent their attempts to break our spirit of resistance with patronizing treats and tacky commercialized Christmassy rubbish...

It's that new posh cow!

What's she on about now?

Brothers!.. As you know, I am a political prisoner... but then, in a way, as victims of society, so are all of you...

Who's he?

It's that new guy... The one who looks like a nonce.

...So I'm sure, like me you want to fight the prison authorities' attempt to poison us with dead flesh, junk food and alcohol...

... So you'll be pleased to hear that I took advantage of my cleaning shift in the prison mailroom this morning to destroy all the deliveries of Christmas cards and presents that they were planning to force on us... Let's say NO to Christmas!

... During my shift in the prison kitchen this morning I threw out all the turkey corpses, cholesterol filled sausages, sugar laden puddings and brain-rotting beer and instead I rustled up a simple but wholesome Garlic and Porridge Oat Bake... Happy Mid-Winter Festival, one and all!

THANKS FOR THIS, MILLIE, I'VE TRIED ABSOLOUTELY EVERYONE. IT'S JUST FOR THIS AFTERNOON...THESE ARE HER THINGS, IF YOU JUST PUT ON THE LION KING VIDEO SHE'LL BE NO TROUBLE.

RIGHT. MUST DASH. YOU'LL BE OKAY, WON'T YOU, AMY?

MUMMY, I DON'T LIKE THIS SCARY MAN.

I'M NOT A SCARY MAN, I'M YOUR MOTHER'S SISTER. YOU CAN CALL ME AUNTIE MILLIE.

NO. COME TO THINK OF IT, THAT'S GENDER STEREOTYPING, hmm....

...YOU'D BETTER CALL ME UNCLTIE MILLIE, THAT DOESN'T PRE-JUDGE EITHER OF OUR SEXES, OR OUR GENDER PREFERENCES.

AND FOR A START YOU CAN FORGET THIS WARMONGERING PRO-MONARCHIST REACTIONARY BRAINWASH!

UH!? FLIP!

HERE, YOU CAN WATCH THIS TAPE I'VE PREPARED. IT'S A CONTINUOUS LOOP OF GERMAINE GREER'S INCREASINGLY BIZZARE RAMBLINGS ON 'LATE REVIEW'. I'VE EDITED ALL THE MEN OUT, SO YOU WON'T FEEL THREATENED.

BOOO-HOOO! NOT FAIR!

ANYWAY, THAT'S FOR WHEN WE COME BACK.

ARE WE GOING TO THE SHOPS?

WE ARE GOING ON A FIELD TRIP.

WE ARE GOING TO EXPLORE THE TOWN CENTRE AND WEIGH UP ALL THE EVIDENCE, AND FROM IT, DEDUCE EXACTLY WHY WE HATE MEN.

SO, IN TOWN...

LOOK! 'MISS SELFRIDGE', THE WORD 'MISS' IMPLIES VIRGINITY, THIS SHOP THEREFORE HAS BEEN CREATED BY MEN AS A MASTURBATORY FANTASY. SO THAT'S WHY WE DON'T SHOP THERE.

THEY'RE NICE BOOTS.

TOP MAN! ...MAN! ... ON TOP! ON TOP OF A WOMAN! ...WHAT'S HE DOING TO HER?!...

IT'S DISGUSTING!

TOP MAN

UH!?

H.M.V.! ... HIS MASTER'S VOICE! NOT HER! HIS! ... MASTER'S VOICE! MASTER AND SLAVE! MAN AS MASTER! MASTER-BATE!... VOICE! VOICE OF A MAN MASTURBATING OVER A SLAVE WOMAN!

HMV

OOOOH! THEY'VE GOT THE SPICE-GIRLS' NEW SINGLE!

TWO HOURS LATER...

FREEMAN-HARDY-WILLIS! FREEMAN: MAN, FREE TO RAPE! HARDY: HARD-ON, DISGUSTING PHALLUS. WILLIS: WILLIES, BIG FAT, THROBBING WILLIES, LONG ONES, GREAT HUGE VEINY ONES, HAIRY... YES! HAIRY ONES! BIG ONES, SMALL ONES, SOME AS BIG AS YOUR HEAD, GIVE 'EM A TWIST; A FLICK O' THE WRIST...

10 MINUTES LATER...

ARE YOU OKAY NOW, UNCLTIE MILLIE?

YES! YES! I'M OKAY! BUT DO YOU SEE NOW?

CAN I GET YOU ANYTHING ELSE AT ALL?

YOU CAN GET ME THE MANAGER...

ERM... WIMMINAGER!

IS SOMETHING NOT TO YOUR LIKING?

DON'T PATRONISE ME! LOOK A THAT'! LOOK AT IT! 'PARENT AND BABY ROOM' IS BLATANT STEREOTYPING OF WIMMIN IN A SUBSERVIENT ROLE!

PARENT & BABY

DADS CAN GO IN THERE TOO, IT SAYS 'PARENT' AND BABY.

IT'S AN OUTRAGE! WE SHOULD BE RE-CLAIMING THAT ROOM! IT SHOULD BE A 'MOTHER AND FEMALE CHILD ONLY ROOM'!...

... NO IT SHOULDN'T!

WIMMIN SHOULD BE FREE TO BREAST-FEED ANYWHERE! IT'S DEGRADING TO SUGGEST THAT IT MUST BE DONE BEHIND CLOSED DOORS... AS IF IT WERE AN ACT OF SHAME!

I DEMAND THE RIGHT TO FEED THIS CHILD... HERE! AND NOW!

HONESTLY.

BUT UNCLTIE MILLIE, I'M TEN AND I'VE GOT A COKE WITH TWO STRAWS.

SHUT-UP! YOU'RE BEING AGEIST! THIS IS AN ISSUE THAT NEEDS TO BE ADDRESSED, AND YOU'RE ONLY TEN SO YOU HAVE NO RIGHT TO COMMENT.

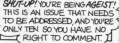

SHORTLY...

WELL! ... WELL!

OH, I'M SORRY, I BEG YOUR PARDON?

FINISHED STARING HAVE YOU?!

?

EXCUSE ME, BUT I'M AFRAID WE OPERATE A DRESS CODE. I MUST INSIST THAT YOU PUT A SHIRT ON, SIR.

FFFPHH!

FLOOMFF!

20 THINGS YOU NEVER KNEW ABOUT SPACE

IN 1998, the Americans celebrated Bonfire Night by sending 77-year old pioneer astronaut John Glenn up into space on a rocket. Meanwhile, moonwalker Buzz Aldrin says that in 30 years time, we'll all be playing golf on Mars. But how much do we actually know about space? Here's a Cape Canaveral countdown of twenty things you never knew about the world's favourite infinite vacuum.

Neil Armstrong climbs up the ladder to get into Saturn V.

20... The first man in space was the Russian Cosmonaut, Yuri Gagarin who blasted off in Sputnik One with his dog Laika on October 10th 1965. The biggest problem he faced was that when cooking his breakfast in space, his sausages stuck to the bottom of the frying pan. Space boffins back on Earth solved this by inventing Teflon, which was used on the oven-to-tableware on all subsequent moonshots.

Some tupperware.

19... Our solar system contains nine planets which are blown around the Sun by solar winds. They are Mars, Venus, the Moon, Neptune, Mercury, Saturn, Haleys Comet, Uranus and Pluto.

Yuri Gagarin in his space hat.

18... And Jupiter. So that makes ten.

17... In olden days, people used to think that the moon was made of green cheese. However, thanks to technology and space travel we now know that it is made of moonrock, a type of weightless grey, fluffy dust, a bit like cement.

16... The closest star to the earth is Alpha Century. No one knows how far away it is, but space eggheads have calculated that it would take you approximately 3,000,000 years to get there.

15... Many labour saving devices used around the home came about as spin-offs from the technology developed for the space race, including polystyrene ceiling tiles, cat flaps, car alarms and tupperware.

14... Light from the pole star Polaris takes 400 years travelling at the speed of light to reach the Earth. That means that when you look at it today, you are actually seeing it as Sir Walter Raleigh saw it when he was a boy.

13... The Space Shuttle is a kind of space bus, and like ordinary buses, you even have to give up your seat for an elderly person. However, real buses seldom explode forty seconds after leaving the bus stop.

12... The Shuttle is the most expensive mode of transport in the world, guzzling petrol at a rate of 6 miles to the gallon. Travel on it is beyond the pocket of most people, a day return to the moon costing a staggering £30,000, the price of two estate cars!

11... The first man to land on the moon was the American Neil 'Stretch' Armstrong, whose command module Saturn V touched down on the beach next to the Sea of Tranquility on July 21st, 1969. During the flight, he passed his time by writing an historic quote to accompany his big moment stepping onto the lunar surface. However, as he marched out, he fluffed his lines and asked the driver, Buzz 'John' Aldrin to go back and land again.

10... The first man in space wasn't a man at all. He was a monkey called Cheetah. In a specially built little rocket full of bananas, he blasted off from the Baikonur Cosmodrome, Kazakhstan on November 3rd 1957. Travelling at 17,750 mph he reached an altitude of 588 miles before blowing up.

Astro chimp Cheetah, bids farewell to his proud mum.

9... Because it is so far away, space cannot be seen with the naked eye. Astrologers, the technical term for space scientists who live in round houses called conservatories, are only able to look at it with the aid of very long glasses called telescopes.

8... The biggest telescope in the world isn't actually in the world at all. It's in space! The Hubble Space Telescope weighs 11 tons, cost $1.5 billion and was flown up into space on the Shuttle. However, when the man looked through the end he couldn't see anything and they had to take it back to the shop.

7... The arthur of Space 1999, Author Seaclarke tells everyone that he conceived the idea of the communication satellite. What he tends not to mention is that he also said they would probably be tied to the ground with very long ropes so as you could climb up and mend them when they broke.

6... Thanks to Mr. Seaclarke's invention, we can now watch 1970's Bavarian pornography on a Wednesday and Saturday, buy nasty jewellery from some failed soap star 24 hours a day and pay an extra tenner to watch Evander Holyfield getting his ear bitten off by a bull-necked rapist.

5... Space is the subject of the oldest and most uninteresting programme on telly. The Sky at Night, presented by fat, boggly-eyed, dusty suited, comedy xylophone player Patrick Moore, was first shown on April 24th 1957 and has appeared, unwatched, every month since.

4... Holidaying is the term for going on holiday, but mooning is not the term for going to the moon. Mooning actually means showing your arse from the back of a bus to two pensioners doing 40mph in a Morris Marina as you overtake them on the motorway.

3... A space bar isn't a pub in space where Whoopee Goldberg sells blue fizzy drinks to things with plastic foreheads and gills. It's the long plastic bit at the bottom of a typewriter that makes holes in your writing.

2... Black holes are enormous space vacuum cleaners. They are so heavy, that a teaspoon full of black hole would weigh as much as a baby elephant and would almost certainly break the spoon.

1... If someone tells you they are going moonwalking it doesn't necessarily mean they are going to blast off in a rocket for a stroll around the lunar surface. It

Some Michael Jacksons.

probably means they are going to do that ridiculous backwards-cum-forwards walk made popular by not-plastic-surgery-nightmare, not-kiddie-diddler, high-pitched knacker grabber Michael Jackson.

ROGER MELLIE
FTV

BEFORE TODAY'S EPISODE OF 'JOLLY ROGER', HERE IS A BRIEF ANNOUNCEMENT

YOU MAY HAVE READ IN THE NEWSPAPERS THAT ROGER MELLIE, ONE OF THE PRESENTERS OF JOLLY ROGER, HAS USED AN ILLEGAL DRUG.

WE HAVE DECIDED THAT AFTER DOING SUCH A NAUGHTY, BAD THING...

...ROGER CANNOT CONTINUE AS A PRESENTER ON THE SHOW. HE IS VERY SORRY FOR WHAT HE HAS DONE, FOR LETTING HIMSELF, AND EVERYONE DOWN...

...AND HE AGREED WITH OUR DECISION TO SACK HIM

DID I FUCK! IT TOOK FIVE SECURITY GUARDS TO DRAG ME OFF THE SET, TOM!

CALM DOWN, ROGER

FUCKIN' HYPOCRITES! HALF THE STAFF AT FTV ARE ON DRUGS! THEY'RE ALL AT IT. AND I SHOULD KNOW, TOM. I SUPPLY MOST OF THEM

WELL SHAME ON YOU

COME ON, TOM. WHY DO YOU THINK THEY SENT ME ON THE JOLLY ROGER SPECIAL ASSIGNMENT TO COLOMBIA?

I NEVER SAW THAT ROGER. IT NEVER GOT SHOWN

WHY?

I DON'T KNOW IF YOU'VE DONE A PIECE TO CAMERA ON A RICKSHAW WITH 4 KILO'S OF SNOW UP YOUR ARSE, TOM... IT'S NOT GOOD TELEVISION!

THE PRODUCER REALLY STUCK HER NECK OUT FOR YOU, ROGER, GIVING YOU THAT BREAK DESPITE YOUR TRACK RECORD. SHE FELT LET DOWN.

...SHE FELT PISSED OFF COS I CUT HER CHARLIE WITH VIM

BUT IT WAS AN HONEST MISTAKE TOM. NOWT TO GET HER TITS IN A TWIST ABOUT

SHE WAS OUT THE COMA IN A WEEK AND I GAVE HER A TWIST OF CRACK AS A GESTURE OF GOOD WILL

DON'T WORRY, TOM. SHE'LL COME BACK ON HER HANDS AND KNEES. JUST YOU WATCH!

...ONCE THAT BALD TWAT OFF THE NEWS MUSCLES IN AND STICKS THE PRICES UP

ANYWAY, WHO GIVES A FLYING FUCK ABOUT TV. IT'S ALL A LOAD OF FUCKING **WANK!**

BESIDES, I'VE GOT MYSELF A NICE LITTLE PANTO LINED UP AT THE TIPTON HIPPODROME – PETER PAN

I NEVER IMAGINED YOU ON STAGE, ROGER.

OOH, YES!

I'VE TROD THE BOARDS WITH THE BEST OF 'EM

I STARTED OFF IN REP IN THE 50'S WITH GOOD OLD MICKEY ASPEL, HUEY SCULLEY AND STUEYPOOS HALL.

THERE'S NOTHING LIKE IT! THE SMELL OF THE GREASEPAINT, THE ROAR OF THE CROWD...

NOT TO MENTION SIX GRAND A WEEK AND ALL THE COCK HUNGRY CHORUS GIRLS YOU CAN HANDLE,

EH!?

I'LL NEVER FORGET THE TIME WE DID 'ALADDIN' AT **THE EMPIRE IN GRIMSBY**...

HA!

I WAS PLAYING TWANKY TO PETER-POO GLAZE'S MAGICIAN. ONE NIGHT, HE MISSED HIS CUE AND CAME IN THE WRONG DOOR. OF COURSE, I CORPSED!

HA! BUT THE FUNNY THING WAS, AFTER THE SHOW, ME AND SID JAMES HAD A TWO'S-UP WITH A 16 YEAR OLD OUT THE CHORUS...

SPLUTTER!

...I WAS FIRST UP, OF COURSE. TURNS OUT, SHE'S NOW ONE OF THE S~~OBSCURED ON LEGAL ADVICE~~S! FANCY THAT, EH, TOM

YEP! I'LL NEVER FORGET THAT NIGHT AS LONG AS I LIVE

...THE DIRTY COW GAVE ME CRABS

WELL, FRANKLY, I'M SURPRISED THEY WANT A DRUG DEALING, DRUNKEN, WIFE BEATER LIKE YOU IN A KIDDIES PANTOMIME

COME OFF IT, TOM. I'M **PERFECT** FOR THE PART. A BIT OF PREVIOUS WILL ADD CREDIBILITY TO MY CAPTAIN HOOK

KIDS AREN'T STUPID, TOM. THEY KNOW WHEN YOU'RE PLAY ACTING. THEY LIKE A **REAL** VILLAIN UP THERE ON STAGE...

I MEAN, TAKE LESLIE GRANTHAM. WHEN HE SHOUTS **"BEHIND YOU"** YOU FUCKING TURN AROUND AND **LOOK!**

HERE, TOM. HERE'S A COUPLE OF TICKETS FOR TOM JUNIOR AND A PAL, ON THE HOUSE! HE'LL ENJOY IT

CHEERS, ROGER. I'LL GIVE 'EM TO HIM...

...WHO ELSE IS IN IT?

THEY'VE REALLY PUSHED THE BOAT OUT, TOM. THERE'S HIM WHO FLOGS THE RINGS ON QVC...THE SMARMY ONE

...ERM...

...AN' THERE'S HIM WHO DOES THE DFS ADVERTS...

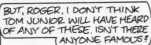

BUT, ROGER, I DON'T THINK TOM JUNIOR WILL HAVE HEARD OF ANY OF THESE. ISN'T THERE ANYONE FAMOUS?

OF COURSE! I'M FORGETTING! THERE'S TOSH LINES. THEY DON'T COME MORE FAMOUS THAN THAT

WHAT!?! YOU MEAN KEVIN LLOYD? BUT HE'S **DEAD,** ROGER

I KNOW, TOM...BUT HE'S GOOD BOX OFFICE, TOM. AND ANYWAY, THEY'VE ALREADY DONE THE POSTERS

LATER...

PSSSST! HEY, KIDS

WANNA SCORE SOME SMACK?

First World War Action

The COWARD of COUNTY ICE-CREAM

Flanders. Row upon row of white tombstones, each one telling its own story of courage and tragedy. But at the end of one of these endless rows stands a stone which tells a story which is stranger than fiction itself.

August 4th, 1914, and war fever grips the nation. General Kitchener mounts a campaign to recruit 100,000 soldiers to be killed in the trenches.

BRITAIN NEEDS CANNON FODDER NOW

County Ice Cream

Have you enlisted, Herbert? They say it'll all be over by Christmas.

No. I'd love to, but somebody has to stay behind and sell ice cream to the women and children.

Over the coming months, Herbert watched and sold ice cream as the men of England packed up their troubles in their old kit bags and marched off to war.

There you are- two Fabs and a Zoom. That's a ha'penny farthing, son.

What would you like, madam?

I'll have a Magnum, please.

Certainly. That's ten bob.

There! That's for you.

Thank you

But Herbert's blood turned as cold as one of his minty stripe choc ices when he unfolded the note.

Gasp!! A white feather!

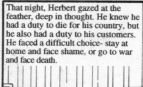

That night, Herbert gazed at the feather, deep in thought. He knew he had a duty to die for his country, but he also had a duty to his customers. He faced a difficult choice- stay at home and face shame, or go to war and face death.

Hello, Herbert, dear. Did you have a good day selling ice cream?

Yes, my dear. And you? Did you have a good day at the Women's Institute?

Yes, wonderful

I've been talking to Mrs. Wilberforce. Her husband Albert has been gassed in the trenches and had his leg blown off. They've given him a medal. Isn't it marvellous?

Erm... yes, dear

She's so proud

That reminds me, we made this for you at the W.I. craft circle

COWARDY COWARDY CUSTARD

It's true! I AM a coward. The Coward of County Ice Cream

For Herbert, this was the final humiliation. He knew what he had to do.

Two days later, and in the trenches at Ypres there is a brief respite in the relentless gunfire.

Tell you what, Billy. When I get back to Blighty, I'm going to take my girl and buy her the biggest ice cream money can buy

Gaw! Ice cream, eh?

Here she is, look, eating a Walls Choc Top Woppa.

That's what I miss most about back home. Ice cream.

You know, sarge, I can almost hear the van. You know, that tinny, distorted theme from Popeye. It takes me right back.

Hang on a mo. I can hear it too.

And me. And it sounds like it's getting nearer.

The battle weary men peered over the top of their trench and could not believe the sight that met their eyes.

Look! it's Herbert!!

County Ice Cream

Soon the battlefield at Ypres rang to the sound of Herbert's annoying chimes.

County Ice Cream

The men lined up for their ice creams. As one fell to the crack of a German shot, another stepped forward to take his place in the queue.

A ninety nine, please, with crushed nuts and monkey's blood

I'll have a blackcurrant split.

After six hours of selling ice cream, Herbert was close to exhaustion.

Jolly good show, old boy! Your plucky ice cream selling has boosted moral no end...

...but I'm afraid you'll have to close your till up now...

...GHQ have sent orders. We're to go over the top just as soon as we've finished our ice creams. Jerry's fire will be pretty heavy, so you'd better get back to Blighty.

And, thank you!

With a heavy heart and a heavy till, Herbert reached inside his pocket for the van key...

...and noticed something flutter to the ground.

Meanwhile...

Right, chaps. Bayonets fixed, gas masks ready, cigarette lighters over hearts...

... and over the top on my whistle.

Suddenly...

It's Herbert! He's driving into no-man's land

Achtung! Einer icenwagen!

Ja! Ja! Schnell

Look! He's distracting the Germans! Quick! Over the top!

Pheeeeep!

Einer neun und neunzig mit minkibluden

Ja! und knacken-nutten, bitte.

Suddenly...

Herbert was killed instantly when his van ran over a mine, but his death was not in vain. His act of bravery allowed the British forces to advance and gain 2 foot 6 inches of mud.

HERBERT A SMITH 1886 – 1916

He was buried with full Dairy Produce Industry honours and his name remembered as a hero, and no longer as the Coward of County ice cream.

THE END

KENNY BALL AND HIS JAZZMAGS

HEH! HEH! I'VE FOUND A LOAD OF TORN-UP NUDIE BOOKS UNDER A HEDGE! ON THE WAY HOME FROM PEBBLE MILL

AH, KENNY! YOUR MOTHER AND I ARE JUST GOING OUT SHOPPING. WILL YOU BE OKAY ON YOUR OWN FOR AN HOUR OR TWO?

OH...ERM...YES! OF COURSE, SNIGGER!

SO...

GOOD. THEY'VE GONE!

NOW TO LOOK AT MY PICS OF BARE LADIES

FRINGLE

THERE!...THAT'S BETTER! THAT ONE'S GOT THE JACKIE DANNY TORN OFF, BUT NEVER MIND

COR!

STRAIGHTEN! STRAIGHTEN!

DING! DONG!

OOER!

HI, KENNY. FANCY COMING TO THE PARK TO PLAY ALEXANDER'S RAGTIME BAND?

NO, I CAN'T TONIGHT, ACKER

ER...I'M DOING MY HOMEWORK

SLAM!

PHEW! THAT WAS NEARLY EMBARRASSING

THERE!...

CLICK! CLICK!

NO MORE INTERRUPTIONS

NOW TO HAVE A RIGHT GOOD BUTCHERS AT THE LADIES' BIG PINK BOSOMS AND THEIR WOTNOTS!

COO-EEE!! IT'S ONLY US, KENNETH

JEEPERS CREEPERS! IT'S MY MAIDEN AUNTS. I'LL NEVER LIVE DOWN THE SHAME IF THEY CATCH ME WITH THESE

WE LET OURSELVES IN THE BACK DOOR

DOOR, YES!

OOH, WHAT ARE YOU READING, KENNETH? IS IT THE PEOPLES FRIEND?

STUFF! STUFF!

FRIEND, YES!

ERM...ERM...OH, ER...

NOW THEN, WHERE ARE MY PEOPLE'S FRIEND GLASSES?

GLASSES, YES!

OH, I THINK I SAW THEM AUNT MILDRED...

...IN THE CELLAR. YOU GO AND HAVE A LOOK FOR THEM

OOH!..

THEM, YES

MIND THE STEPS

...IT'S VERY DARK IN HERE

WHUMP! BUMP! CLUMP! THUMP!

GROAN!..I THINK...GROAN ...I THINK I'VE...BROKEN MY...MY NECK!

NECK, YES!

RIGHT, I'M TAKING MY NODDY BOOKS UP TO MY BEDROOM

SO...

COR! LOOK AT ALL THEM LADIES IN THE RIK!

WRIGGLE! WRIGGLE!

HI, KENNY! WHAT ARE YOU READING?

A COMIC, IS IT? LET'S HAVE A LOOK! I LIKE COMICS

YOIKS! THE WINDOW CLEANER!

SLAM!!

AAAAARGH!

I'LL STUDY MY MUCKY PICS IN THE WARDROBE...

...NOBODY'LL FIND ME IN HERE, SURELY

HEH! HEH! THAT'S BETTER

2 HOURS LATER... DING! DONG!

GET THE DOOR, MOTHER

RIGHT-HO!

SHOP! SHOP!

HELLO, MISSUS. WE'RE COLLECTING OLD FURNITURE FOR THE LOCAL GIRLS SIXTH FORM COLLEGE. DO YOU HAVE ANY SPARE ITEMS?

YES! I'VE GOT AN OLD WARDROBE YOU CAN HAVE

SHORTLY... HURRY ALONG, GIRLS. LET'S GET ALL THIS FURNITURE SORTED OUT

PLEASE, MISS...THERE'S A BOY IN THIS WARDROBE LOOKING AT ALL DIRTY PICTURES

EURRGH!

EH!?

LOOK AT HIM, GIRLS... THE FILTHY BEAST!

SHAME!

'Telly Christmas one and all...

Deck the halls with ♪♪♪ boughs of holly! ♪♪♪ Fa-la-la-la-laaa-la-la-la-lah

Christmas was a wonderful time for Edwin Scrooge and his family. Their home was vibrant with the sounds of a truly joyous family occasion, as they enjoyed the festivities to the full...

LET'S SING ANOTHER DARLING!

I'M SURE WE'D ALL LOVE TO DARLING, BUT THERE'S THE TREE TO DECORATE.

YES! AND THE PUDDINGS TO PREPARE! AND THE YULE LOG TO FETCH!

YES! AND THE CAKE TO ICE! AND THE HOLLY TO GATHER FOR THE WREATH!

IT'S A PITY WE DON'T HAVE TELEVISION FATHER, MY FRIEND BILLY CRATCHET SAYS THERE'S A PROGRAMME ON WHICH THEY MAKE AN ADVENT CROWN WITH CANDLES ON IT!

IT SOUNDS VERY CHRISTMASSY FATHER! CAN WE HAVE A TELEVISION?

HO! HO! HO! TELEVISION? BAH! HUMBUG! WHAT WOULD WE WANT WITH A TELEVISION? WE WOULDN'T HAVE TIME TO WATCH IT, THERE'S SO MANY OTHER THINGS WE COULD BE DOING!

COME ON, EVERYONE AROUND THE LOG FIRE! HANG UP YOUR STOCKINGS AND I'LL READ YOU 'THE NIGHT BEFORE CHRISTMAS'.

OH, *SUPER* FATHER! OUR FAVOURITE!

CAN WE HAVE MINCE PIES TOO?

Later...

TONIGHT SANTA WILL COME, I'M SO EXCITED! GOODNIGHT FATHER, IT'S BEEN A WONDERFUL DAY.

YES, THANK YOU FOR MAKING OUR DAY SO SPECIAL, GOODNIGHT.

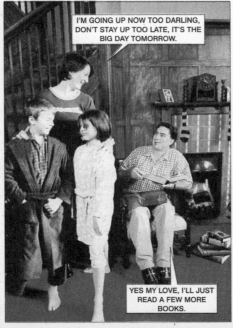

I'M GOING UP NOW TOO DARLING, DON'T STAY UP TOO LATE, IT'S THE BIG DAY TOMORROW.

YES MY LOVE, I'LL JUST READ A FEW MORE BOOKS.

YAWN!

119

Cont. over

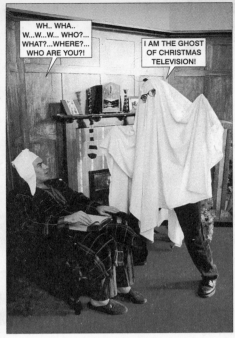

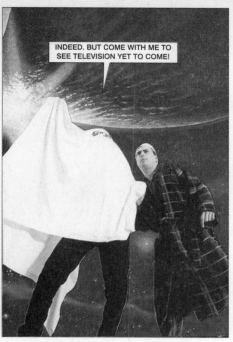

ST.SD.GD.DJ. '98 PHOTOS COLIN DAVISON

THE SID SEXOLOGIST

TYNESIDE'S SILVER-TONGUED CAVALIER

HOW LADS. I'VE SENT OFF FOR THIS BOOK, REET, AN' I'M TELLIN' YUZ NOO, IT'S THE FUCKIN' *FANNY-HUNTER'S BIBLE!*

NINE POOND NINETY-NINE. AALL YA SPONDS BACK IF YER NOT KNEE-DEEP IN GASH IN A FORTNEET.

WHY MAN, THE BLURK WHAT'S WROTE IT SHAGS A DIFFERENT BORD EVERY NEET, AN' HE'S A MILLIONAIRE.

WHY, HE MUST BE CLEVER IF HE LOOKS LIKE BENNY OOT O' CROSSRURDS AN' HE'S HUMPIN' TOP FLAP!

AH AYE, HE'S A *GENIUS!*

Y'SEE HE KNAAS AALL THE SECRETS OF A WOMAN'S MIND, HE'S A PROPER SCIENTIST AN' THAT. HE WROTE LURDS O' BOOKS ON HOW TU WIN ON THE BANDITS AN' EVERYTHING ... FUCKIN' *GENIUS!*

MUST BE WORTH FUCKIN' *MILLIONS!*

AYE SID, THAT'LL BE WHY HE CAN ONLY AFFORD A SQUARE INCH ON PAGE 249 OF THE AUTO-TRADER.

NAAH. THAT'S *REVORSE PSYCOLOGY* MAN, BAZ. IT'S *FORBIDDEN KNOWLEDGE,* YE CANNAT HAVE *THIS* FAALLIN' INTU THE WRANG HANDS.

WHO'S FORBIDDEN IT, LIKE?

THEY MAN, Y'KNAA ...THEM.

AAAH! ... RIGHT.

HOWAY SID! HOWAY! SHOW US!

NAAH, NAAH. I CANNAT SHOW YUZ. I'M SWORN TU SECRECY MAN. I COULDN'T LET YEEZ KNAA AALL THE SECRETS ... YUZ COULD *ENCRURCH* ON ME GOWT MOONTAIN.

HOWAY MAN, AT LEAST TELL US WHAT IT SEZ MAN, SID.

AALL REET, AALL REET. I'LL LEND YUZ IT WHEN ME FUCKIN' COCK'S FAALLEN' OFF!

DIVEN'T BE SUCH A CUNT, SID. LET YER MATES IN ON THIS FUCKIN' *AMAYZIN'* KNOWLEGE.

REET, I'LL GIVE YUZ A TINY BIT TASTER ... THE BOOK SEZ THIS...

WHAT YE HAVE TU DEE IS THIS... MEK THE LASS *WANT* YU, THEN, REET, YE LET 'ER KNAA THAT SHE *CANNAT* HAVE YU. THAT DRIVES 'ER MENTAL. DROONIN' IN 'ER AAN BATTA AN' THAT.

WHAT THE BLURK RECKONS IS IT'S LIKE FISHIN'... YE GIVE THEM A FLASH O' THE BAIT, THEN YE FUCKIN' TORN AN' RUN ... THEN THE CUNT COMES FLEEIN' AFTA YU.

AYE SID, *JUST* LIKE FISHIN' THAT.

SOONDS CANNY SID, BUT HOW EXACTLY D'YU GET THEM TU *WANT* YE IN THE FORST PLACE?

ERM...

FLITTER! FLITTER!

FLITTER-FLIT!

FLITTER! FLITTER!

FLITTER-FLIT!

WELL ... OBVIOUSLY IT DOESN'T TELL YU ABSOLOUTELY *EVERYTHINK,* NAAH, 'SEE THAT WOULD TEK THE FUN OOT THE CHASE.

HAD ON, MEBEEZ THAT'S WHAT *THIS* IS FOR. I GOT THIS HOYED IN FOR NOWT. WELL, I SAY FOR NOWT, I HAD TU PAY THE PURSTAGE AN' PACKIN'. AYE, FAWATY POOND.

HERE LADS, READ THAT LABEL! "WARNING: THIS HORMURN SPRAY GIVES MEN AN UNFAIR ADVANTAGE."

FUCKIN' HELL. IT'S THERE IN BLACK AN' WHITE.

AYE. THEY COULDN'T PUT THAT, COULD THEY, IF IT WASN'T TRUE, LIKE.

HERE! SMELL *THAT!*

SHIT!

JESUS!

FSST!

FUCKIN' HELL!

NOW THAT MIGHT SMELL BAD TO US, YE MIGHT SAY, IT'S NOT ATTRACTIVE TO *US.* IN FACT IT'S A BIT LIKE STALE PISS. BUT, Y'SEE TO A WOMAN... THAT'S *IRRESISTABLE.*

IT'S SUBLIMINAL, Y'KNAA. THEY WON'T EVEN KNAA WHY THEY WANT TO SHAG US.

COUGH! COUGH! COUGH!

COUGH! COUGH! COUGH!

FSSSSSSSSSSSST!

FSSSSSSSSSSSSST!

HERE GANS LADS. WATCH ME AN' TEK NOTES.

COUGH! COUGH! COUGH!

WAFT! WAFT!

HOW PET. NOW I *KNAA* THAT YE WANT TU FUCK US, BUT I'M NOT GANNA *LET* YU. NEE WAY.

UH?!

WAFT!

IS THERE SOME MISTAKE? *ME?* WANT TU FUCK *YOU?!* EVEN IF YOU DIDN'T SMELL LIKE MY GRANDAD'S UNDERPANTS, YOU'RE STILL AN UGLY BRAINLESS LITTLE TWAT...

... NOW *FUCK OFF* OUT OF MY SIGHT YOU FESTERING LITTLE *SHIT.*

SO WHAT IS IT YE DEE NOO SID? YE PLAY HARD-TU-GET THEN, D'YU?

11pm...

EEEH! IS THAT YOUR MATE? HE FUCKIN' STINKS. HAS HE GOT A MEDICAL PROBLEM?

KEEP DOWNWIND OF US, SID. YOU'RE UPSETTIN' THE LASSES WE'VE JUST PULLED.

AYE. MY LASSES NAIL VARNISH IS PEELIN'.

He's a Sneezy Lover

By our Medical Musical Correspondent Dr. Feelgood Stutterford

AS well as contending with aching limbs, runny noses and swollen glands, flu sufferers this winter will face an extra headache - a whopping bill from pop millionaire Phil Collins!

For the baldy Genesis drummer, whose previous investments include fish farms, christmas trees and racehorses, has snapped up all world rights to the influenza virus.

Victims

Unlucky victims will find themselves coughing up an amazing £8.50 a day in royalties to the greedy chart-topping slapster. If this winter's expected epidemic materialises, Collins can look forward to profits of £5000 million billion or more.

The War Song

Collins, 45, acquired the infection privately two weeks ago and immediately leased it to himself via a wholly owned holding company, 'Ill Collins Plc' based in the Channel Islands. City analysts expect profits from the company to double with

Collins - drumming up cash and Norman Dodds (below) - not taking it lying down.

Swollen coughers swell coffers for stumpy tubthumper

this new addition to a portfolio which already boasts veruccas, bad guts and the clap.

The Medal Song

But news of Collins' winter bug buy-out got a cold reception from Norman Dodds, chairman of the National Influenza Sufferers Society. "This is a terrible blow for anyone with a bunged up nose" he told reporters.

It's a Miracle

And Collins is not the only pop star to cash in on peo-

ple's misery. As cases of T.B. increase, has-been trouser-splitting singer P.J. Proby looks forward to a cash windfall, having made what looked like a bad investment when he bought a majority share in the degenerative lung disease in the fifties.

However, illnesses are not always a healthy investment. Ex-Beatle Ringo Starr made a big blunder in 1967 when all his Yellow Submarine royalties sank without trace after he bought smallpox, three weeks before a cure was found. His sole income nowadays comes from ownership of the rights to that pain you get behind your eye if you eat ice cream too quickly.

Karma chameleon

A spokeswoman for Collins last night said, "The number you have dialed has not been recognised. Please replace the handset and try again. Do do dip. Do do dip."

Who's Next?

The Who guitarist Pete Townsend revealed this week how his life was wrecked after the death of the band's drummer, Keith Moon, 20 years ago.

For since that time, the rock legend has lived in fear of a curse developing that would pick the band members off one by one.

Member

"Keith's death could be written off as a one-off thing" he told us yesterday. "But if another band member, say Roger or John were to die, then 'The Curse of The Who' would be a reality, and I could be next."

Tool

The fear of the curse has taken its toll on Townsend. Nervous-looking and a chronic chain smoker, he hasn't left his Rich-

EXCLUSIVE

mond mansion since Moon's death in 1978, except to go out and perform his daily business.

Chopper

But other band members were less worried. "I wouldn't believe in 'The Curse of The Who'" said Roger Daltry, speaking from his fish shop. "It would all be a load of scaremongery and mumbo jumbo."

John Thomas

Bass guitarist John Entwistle was less sceptical, however. "The series

The Who - no hex please, we're Brit-pop.

of deaths would probably be a coincidence rather than a curse." he told us. "But being a superstitious

person I'd probably be a bit more careful when crossing the road or eating fish bones."

THAT DOOR IS TOO BIG

MY WIFE LIKES TO MAKE A GRAND ENTRANCE

Tea man arrested

A 45-year-old Lincolnshire librarian was last night charged with sweetening a cup of tea left on a worktop by his mother.

Graham McBride of Bardney Old Cottages, Woodhall Spa stands accused of adding one or more teaspoonfuls of sugar to the tea, belonging to Mrs. Brenda McBride, 70, of

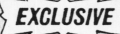

An angry McBride is led away by police.

the same address, making it unpalatable to her. A further charge of sipping the tea may also be brought if the results of forensic tests prove positive.

Statement

A short police statement issued this morning read, "At 2.30a.m., Graham McBride was charged with sweetening tea on the 15th November this year. We also wish to speak to him about a sipping offence, and he has been detained for further questioning."

Overdraft

Mrs. McBride was unavailable for comment today, but a neighbour who did not wish to be named told reporters that she had been visibly shaken on the day of the incident. "The first thing we knew about it was when the police cars pulled into the close," she said. "This isn't the sort of thing you expect around here."

Queueues

In 1956, Mr. McBride's father, Ernest, then 30, was hanged after being found guilty of stirring his tea with the sugar spoon, and then replacing it in the bowl when it was all wet.

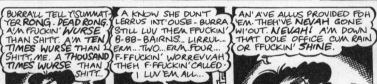

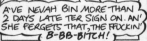

DIANA ROSS'S DOGSHIT MUSEUM

POP SUPERSTAR DIANA ROSS WAS EMBARKED ON A MOST REMARKABLE JOURNEY

FOR SHE WAS DRIVING HER FANTASTIC TRAVELLING MUSEUM OF DOGSHIT ACROSS THE ALPS TO SWITZERLAND

THE EX-SUPREME'S TWO COMPANIONS WERE YOUNG ORPHANS TIM AND JANICE HAMPSON, WHO HAD RUN AWAY FROM THEIR ORPHANAGE TO JOIN THE DOGSHIT MUSEUM

IT'S GETTING PRETTY COLD IN THESE MOUNTAINS, DIANA ROSS

I ONLY HOPE YOUR DOG TURDS DON'T ICE OVER

DON'T WORRY, TIM

WE'LL STOP OVERNIGHT AT THIS LITTLE BAVARIAN VILLAGE

THE THREE FRIENDS OPENED UP THE MUSEUM IN THE VILLAGE SQUARE AND BEFORE LONG A LARGE CROWD HAD GATHERED

ROLL UP, ROLL UP. COME AND SEE EUROPE'S EIGHTH LARGEST COLLECTION OF DOGS EGGS

WE HAVE NEARLY SIXTEEN SPECIMENS, EACH ONE PERFECTLY FORMED AND ABSOLUTELY MINGING

THE DOGSHIT MUSEUM WAS SOON DOING A ROARING TRADE

LATER, AT CLOSING TIME

WHEW! WHAT A BUSY DAY

WHY DON'T WE STAY HERE FOR A WEEK OR SO, DIANA ROSS. YOUR MUSEUM WOULD BRING IN A FORTUNE

JUST THEN AN ANCIENT BAVARIAN PEASANT APPROACHED

STAY HERE BY ALL MEANS, MY FOREIGN FRIENDS. BUT BEWARE...

FOR THESE MOUNTAINS ARE INHABITED BY VAMPIRES AND ABOMINABLE SNOWMANS AND THAT. AND, ACCORDING TO LOCAL LEGEND, THEY'RE REALLY SCARY AND WILL COME AND GET YOU

DON'T LET HIM WORRY YOU, CHILDREN. THAT'S JUST AN OLD BAVARIAN SUPERSTITION

COME ON — LET'S GET SOME SLEEP

BUT EARLY NEXT MORNING TIM AND JENNY HEARD A SCREAM COME FROM INSIDE THE MUSEUM

SHRIEK!

DIANA ROSS'S DOGSHIT MUSEUM

WHAT TH— THAT'S DIANA ROSS!

(SOB) MY BEAUTIFUL DOG SHIT MUSEUM HAS BEEN VANDALISED!

SOMEONE — OR SOMETHING — CAME IN DURING THE NIGHT AND WRECKED ALL THE EXHIBITS

MY PRECIOUS TURDS HAVE BEEN STREWN ACROSS THE FLOOR AND TRODDEN ON. SOME OF THE CRUMBLY ONES HAVE ALL BROKEN UP

AND LOOK — THERE'S ONE THAT'S HAD A LOLLY-STICK STUCK INTO IT

I WARNED YOU, MY FOREIGN FRIENDS. IT WAS ALL THEM MONSTERS AND YETIS THAT SMASHED UP YOUR MUSEUM

(SHUDDER) PERHAPS THE OLD MAN IS TELLING THE TRUTH — PERHAPS IT WAS MONSTERS

I THINK NOT. ONE OF THE VANDALISED EXHIBITS HAS A BICYCLE TYRE TRACK THROUGH IT

WHAT KIND OF YETI WOULD RIDE A BICYCLE?

AND LOOK — SOMEBODY HAS BEEN SCRAPING THEIR BE-SHITTED SHOE ALL THE WAY UP THE KERB

THE TRAIL LEADS UP INTO THE MOUNTAINS — LET'S FOLLOW IT

THE FRIENDS SET OFF UP THE STEEP MOUNTAIN ROAD

BUT DIANA ROSS, WHY WOULD ANYONE WANT TO DESTROY YOUR DOGSHIT MUSEUM

THAT'S WHAT I INTEND TO FIND OUT, JANICE

SUDDENLY

LOOK OUT! THAT TRUCK JUST APPEARED FROM NOWHERE

GLADYS KNIGHT'S CATSHIT CURIO COLLECTION

IT-IT'S TRYING TO FORCE US OFF THE ROAD

GLADYS KNIGHT! SO IT WAS YOU ALL ALONG

THIS MOUNTAIN RANGE ISN'T BIG ENOUGH FOR BOTH OF US, DIANA ROSS — SO NOW I'M GOING TO PUSH YOU OVER THE CLIFF-EDGE

BUT DIANA ROSS JAMMED ON THE BRAKES, SENDING GLADYS KNIGHT AND HER COLLECTION OF CATSHIT CURIOS OVER THE CLIFF

HONK HO-O-NK

SCREECH!

AIEEEE!

SHE — SHE'S GONE, CHILDREN

GLADYS KNIGHT HAS BEEN PIPPED AT THE POST

BOOM!

COME ALONG. LET'S CONTINUE ON OUR JOURNEY TO SWITZERLAND

AND SO

...AIN'T NO MOUNTAIN HI-I-IGH ENOUGH...